Standardized Test Practice
Teacher Edition
earth.msscience.com

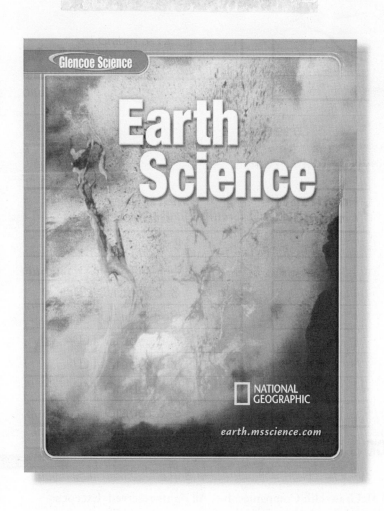

Glencoe Science

Earth Science

NATIONAL GEOGRAPHIC

earth.msscience.com

D1230824

 **Glencoe**

New York, New York   Columbus, Ohio   Chicago, Illinois   Peoria, Illinois   Woodland Hills, California

 Glencoe

The **McGraw-Hill** Companies

Send all inquiries to:
Glencoe/McGraw-Hill
8787 Orion Place
Columbus, OH 43240-4027

ISBN 0-07-866965-0

Printed in the United States of America.

1 2 3 4 5 6 7 8 9 10   009   09 08 07 06 05 04

Contents

Introduction

The Teacher Edition

Welcome to the Teacher Edition of *Standardized Test Practice* for *Glencoe Earth Science*.

This Teacher Edition is comprised of three distinct sections:

- ### Introduction: Methods

  The Teacher Edition Introduction contains methods for content review and test preparation, answer sheets for student use, a complete list of the National Science Standards skills, and answer keys that provide the correct answer choice and the National Science Standard skill tested for each question.

- ### Chapter Test: Content Mastery

  For every chapter in *Glencoe Earth Science*, this workbook contains a Chapter Test. The Chapter Tests **do not** test students' comprehensive retention of chapter content but **do** test students' mastery of chapter content. Chapter Tests are included in the Student Edition. Correct answer choices can be found in the answer key on pages xii–xxi of the Teacher Edition.

- ### Standardized Test Practice: Test Preparation

  For every chapter in *Glencoe Earth Science*, this workbook contains a corresponding Standardized Test Practice. The questions in the Standardized Test Practices help prepare students for national tests such as the TerraNova, the Iowa Tests of Basic Skills (ITBS), and the Stanford Achievement Test, Ninth Edition (SAT-9). These Standardized Test Practices are included in the Student Edition. Correct answer choices can be found in the answer key on pages xii–xxi of the Teacher Edition.

How can this workbook help my students on standardized tests?

By beginning to prepare your students **now** for their upcoming standardized tests, you will greatly improve their chances of success. This workbook will help your students become accustomed to **answering both multiple-choice questions and open-ended response questions like those on the TerraNova, ITBS, and SAT-9.** Questions requiring students to eliminate answer choices based on information provided in graphs, illustrations, and tables also are included.

Items covering general science concepts provide a thorough representation of the National Science Standards.

A unique four-part **Task Regimen** and helpful **Test-Taking Tips** designed to maximize the benefits of using this workbook are presented in this section.

Some of the activities in the tables are designed to encourage interaction between students of various levels.

Task Regimen

Task I

Objective: To use the Standardized Test Practices to strengthen students' approaches to questions, to teach techniques for answering questions, and to prepare students for standardized tests

In-Class Assignment: To give students the opportunity to be exposed to realistic standardized-testing situations

At-home Assignment: To enable students to analyze their own mistakes and identify any skills that need extra review

LEVEL	In-Class Assignment	At-Home Assignment
LEVEL 1	Using the Standardized Test Practices, administer a practice test in realistic test-taking setting. Make sure to announce the in-class, practice "test day" in advance so that students can prepare. **Benefit:** *Students become more familiar with a realistic test-taking atmosphere.*	Students review their wrong answers, identify their mistakes, and try to figure out the correct answers, using the textbook only when needed. **Benefit:** *Students closely analyze their answer choices and learn to identify mistakes or common habits such as working too fast or not reading questions carefully.*
LEVEL 2	Same as above. **Benefit:** Same as above.	Same as above. **Benefit:** *Same as above.*
LEVEL 3	Same as above. **Benefit:** *Same as above.*	Students review their wrong answers, identify their mistakes, and try to figure out the correct answers, using the textbook for every question. They should put a question mark next to any questions that they still cannot answer. These particularly difficult questions should be reviewed with a partner or during class time. **Benefit:** *Students closely analyze their answer choices, learn to identify mistakes or common habits, and thoroughly review material in the textbook.*

Task II

Objective: To use the Chapter Tests and Standardized Test Practices to review science material and prepare for standardized tests

In-Class Assignments: To help students better understand the scientific concepts and details that they were not clear on after completion of the textbook chapter

At-Home Assignments: To identify what parts of the textbook provide the information students need to correct misunderstanding of scientific concepts

LEVEL	At-Home Assignment	In-Class Assignment
LEVEL 1	After working on a practice test in a realistic test-taking setting, students note the textbook page number where the information can be found and prepare some brief questions for other students to help them understand the material. Students can pursue their scientific investigations independently in the library. **Benefit:** *Students work to have an advanced understanding of the scientific material.*	In small groups, students can review missed concepts and work on the brief questions prepared by peers. **Benefit:** *Students solidify their understanding of material by working with their peers and having an opportunity to be part of a more focused review.*
LEVEL 2	After working on a practice test, students can make a list of all information that is required to answer each missed question and note the textbook page number where the information can be found. **Benefits:** *Students are able to review material they had learned and try to find the source of their error.*	Same as above. **Benefit:** *Same as above.*
LEVEL 3	After working on a practice test, students can make a list of all information that is required to answer each missed question and note the textbook page number where the information can be found. For instance, when students cannot locate the textbook information, they should write down a list of the questions that they need to better understand. **Benefit:** *Students help themselves by locating material in the textbook that relates to the test questions. By writing out a list of problematic questions, students create an organized goal and review system for themselves.*	In small groups, students can review missed concepts and work on the brief questions prepared by peers. Review the problematic questions with the group. Then reread the missed questions and determine why they were wrong on the first test. **Benefit:** *Same as above.*

Task III

Objective: To focus on the process of elimination by practicing with the Chapter Tests and Standardized Test Practices

In-Class Assignments: To clarify and illustrate common patterns and methods that can be used to effectively eliminate wrong answer choices

At-home Assignments: To develop the ability to eliminate incorrect answer choices through careful analysis and description

LEVEL	At-Home Assignment	In-Class Assignment
LEVEL 1	Students should write a list of the hardest questions with graphics and all the information given in the questions and accompanying graphics. Students should note which pieces of information are helpful in answering the question correctly. ***Benefit:*** *Students practice identifying and organizing all of the information given in test questions.*	Review test questions as an entire class or in groups. Students' observations of the information given by each question and its accompanying graphic should be written on the board. ***Benefit:*** *Students practice thinking critically about the information given in questions and graphics.*
LEVEL 2	Students should write a list of the hardest questions with graphics and all the information given in the questions and accompanying graphics. Students should note which pieces of information are helpful in answering the question correctly. Students should use the textbook whenever necessary. ***Benefit:*** *Students practice identifying and organizing all of the information given in test questions.*	Review test questions as an entire class or in groups. Students' observations of the information given by each question and its accompanying graphic should be written on the board. ***Benefit:*** *Same as above.*
LEVEL 3	Students should write a list of the hardest questions with graphics and all the information given in the questions and accompanying graphics. Students should note any questions or problems they had with understanding the graphics. ***Benefit:*** *Students practice identifying and organizing all of the information given in test questions.*	Review test questions as an entire class or in groups. Students' observations of the information given by each question and its accompanying graphic should be written on the board. For particularly difficult questions, students should work in small groups to create thorough lists of observations and questions. ***Benefit:*** *Same as above.*

Task IV

Objective: To develop the ability to recognize, extract, and use all information given within the test

In-Class Assignments: To discuss and identify effective mechanisms for recognizing all information given in test questions and graphics

At-Home Assignments: To develop the ability to recognize and use all of the given information in test questions and graphics

LEVEL	At-Home Assignment	In-Class Assignment
LEVEL 1	Students should write a list of the hardest questions with graphics and all the information given in the questions and accompanying graphics. Students should note which pieces of information are helpful in answering the question correctly. **Benefit:** *Students practice identifying and organizing all of the information given in test questions.*	Review test questions as an entire class or in groups. Students' observations of the information given by each question and its accompanying graphic should be written on the board. **Benefit:** *Students practice thinking critically about the information given in questions and graphics.*
LEVEL 2	Students should write a list of the hardest questions with graphics and all the information given in the questions and accompanying graphics. Students should note which pieces of information are helpful in answering the question correctly. Students should use the textbook whenever necessary. **Benefit:** *Students practice identifying and organizing all of the information given in test questions.*	Review test questions as an entire class or in groups. Students' observations of the information given by each question and its accompanying graphic should be written on the board. **Benefit:** *Same as above.*
LEVEL 3	Students should write a list of the hardest questions with graphics and all the information given in the questions and accompanying graphics. Students should note any questions or problems they had with understanding the graphics. **Benefit:** *Students practice identifying and organizing all of the information given in test questions.*	Review test questions as an entire class or in groups. Students' observations of the information given by each question and its accompanying graphic should be written on the board. For particularly difficult questions, students should work in small groups to create thorough lists of observations and questions. **Benefit:** *Same as above.*

Test-Taking Tips

Test-Taking Tips for _Before the Test_:

- Remind students to get 8–9 hours of sleep for several days leading up to the test.

- Advise students to spend the evening prior to the test doing something relaxing such as playing a board game, exercising, or reading an enjoyable book.

- Encourage students to eat a healthy breakfast high in protein, fresh foods, and carbohydrates. Suggest that students bring granola bars and juice if they will be getting a break during the test.

- The morning of the test, tell students to clear their minds of any outside distractions and focus their attention on the test.

Test-Taking Tips for _During the Test_:

- Instruct students to listen and read all directions in order to avoid errors due to misunderstanding.

- Remind students to be sure that they understand the question before reading the answer choices. Once they get to the answer choices, they should always read every answer choice before selecting an answer.

- Graphics often contain crucial information. Remind students to examine and analyze all graphics related to a question.

- Explain to students that they should always choose an answer. By eliminating as many wrong choices as possible, students have a good chance at guessing correctly and obtaining more points.

National Science Standards

(UCP) *Unifying Concepts and Processes*
1 Systems, order, and organization
2 Evidence, models, and explanation
3 Change, constancy, and measurement
4 Evolution and equilibrium
5 Form and function

(A) *Science as Inquiry*
1 Abilities necessary to do scientific inquiry
2 Understanding scientific inquiry

(B) *Physical Science: Grades 5–8*
1 Properties and changes of properties in matter
2 Motions and forces
3 Transfer of energy

(B) *Physical Science: Grades 9–12*
1 Structure of atoms
2 Structure and properties of matter
3 Chemical reactions
4 Motions and forces
5 Conservation of energy and increase in disorder
6 Interactions of energy and matter

(C) *Life Science: Grades 5–8*
1 Structure and function in living systems
2 Reproduction and heredity
3 Regulation and behavior
4 Populations and ecosystems
5 Diversity and adaptations of organisms

(C) *Life Science: Grades 9–12*
1 The cell
2 Molecular basis of heredity
3 Biological evolution
4 Interdependence of organisms
5 Matter, energy, and organization in living systems
6 Behavior of organisms

(D) *Earth and Space Science: Grades 5–8*
1 Structure of the Earth system
2 Earth's history
3 Earth in the solar system

(D) *Earth and Space Science: Grades 9–12*
1 Energy in the Earth system
2 Geochemical cycles
3 Origin and evolution of the Earth system
4 Origin and evolution of the universe

(E) *Science and Technology: Grades 5–8*
1 Abilities of technological design
2 Understanding science and technology

(E) *Science and Technology: Grades 9–12*
1 Abilities of technological design
2 Understanding science and technology

(F) *Science in Personal and Social Perspectives: Grades 5–8*
1 Personal health
2 Populations, resources, and environments
3 Natural hazards
4 Risks and benefits
5 Science and technology in society

(F) *Science in Personal and Social Perspectives: Grades 9–12*
1 Personal and community health
2 Population growth
3 Natural resources
4 Environmental quality
5 Natural and human-induced hazards
6 Science and technology in local, national, and global challenges

(G) *History and Nature of Science: Grades 5–8*
1 Science as a human endeavor
2 Nature of science
3 History of science

(G) *History and Nature of Science: Grades 9–12*
1 Science as a human endeavor
2 Nature of scientific knowledge
3 Historical perspectives

Answer Key

Chapter 1: The Nature of Science

Chapter Test

Question Number	Correct Answer	National Science Standard
1.	a.	A1 Grades 5–12
2.	h.	A1 Grades 5–12
3.	d.	A1 Grades 5–12
4.	h.	A1 Grades 5–12
5.	b.	A1 Grades 5–12
6.	g.	A1 Grades 5–12

Standardized Test Practice

Question Number	Correct Answer
1	B
2	H
3	A
4	G
5	C
6	G
7	See page xxiv.

Chapter 2: Matter

Chapter Test

Question Number	Correct Answer	National Science Standard
1.	d.	B1 Grades 5–9
2.	h.	A1 Grades 5–12
3.	c.	B1 Grades 5–9
4.	h.	B1 Grades 5–9
5.	b.	B1 Grades 5–9
6.	h.	B1 Grades 5–9
7.	b.	B1 Grades 5–9

Standardized Test Practice

Question Number	Correct Answer
1	A
2	J
3	C
4	F
5	A
6	J
7	See page xxiv.

Chapter 3: Minerals

Chapter Test

Question Number	Correct Answer	National Science Standard
1.	d.	B1 Grades 5–8
2.	h.	B1 Grades 5–8
3.	c.	B1 Grades 5–8
4.	g.	B1 Grades 5–8
5.	a.	B1 Grades 5–8
6.	h.	B1 Grades 5–8
7.	d.	B1 Grades 5–8

Standardized Test Practice

Question Number	Correct Answer
1	C
2	F
3	D
4	H
5	B
6	J
7	A
8	G

Chapter 4: Rocks

Chapter Test

Question Number	Correct Answer	National Science Standard
1.	c.	B1 Grades 5–8
2.	g.	B1 Grades 5–8
3.	a.	B1 Grades 5–8
4.	j.	A1 Grades 5–12
5.	c.	B1 Grades 5–8
6.	j.	B1 Grades 5–8

Standardized Test Practice

Question Number	Correct Answer
1	A
2	H
3	C
4	J
5	A
6	G
7	B

Chapter 5: Earth's Eneregy and Mineral Resources

Chapter Test

Question Number	Correct Answer	National Science Standard
1.	b.	F3 Grades 5–8
2.	j.	A1 Grades 5–12
3.	a.	F3 Grades 5–8
4.	g.	F2 Grades 5–8
5.	c.	F2 Grades 5–8
6.	g.	B1 Grades 5–8
7.	a.	F2 Grades 5–8

Standardized Test Practice

Question Number	Correct Answer
1	C
2	G
3	D
4	G
5	C
6	F
7	See page xxiv.

Chapter 6: Views of Earth

Chapter Test

Question Number	Correct Answer	National Science Standard
1.	d.	D1 Grades 5–8
2.	h.	UCP1 Grades 5–12
3.	b.	D1 Grades 5–8
4.	h.	D3 Grades 5–8
5.	a.	D1 Grades 5–8

Standardized Test Practice

Question Number	Correct Answer
1	B
2	G
3	A
4	G
5	A
6	J
7	A

Chapter 7: Weathering and Soil

Chapter Test

Question Number	Correct Answer	National Science Standard
1.	d.	B1 Grades 5–8
2.	g.	F2 Grades 5–8
3.	d.	F2 Grades 5–8
4.	h.	F2 Grades 9–12
5.	d.	F2 Grades 5–8
6.	h.	F2 Grades 5–8
7.	b.	F5 Grades 5–8
8.	j.	F5 Grades 5–8

Standardized Test Practice

Question Number	Correct Answer
1	A
2	H
3	C
4	G
5	C
6	F
7	See page xxiv.
8	See page xxiv.

Chapter 8: Erosional Forces

Chapter Test

Question Number	Correct Answer	National Science Standard
1.	c.	D1 Grades 5–8
2.	h.	F3 Grades 5–8
3.	c.	D1 Grades 5–8
4.	g.	F3 Grades 5–8
5.	a.	F3 Grades 5–8
6.	g.	D1 Grades 5–8
7.	a.	D1 Grades 5–8
8.	h.	A1 Grades 5–12
9.	c.	D1 Grades 5–8
10.	f.	D1 Grades 5–8

Standardized Test Practice

Question Number	Correct Answer
1	D
2	G
3	D
4	H
5	B
6	See page xxiv.
7	See page xxiv.

Chapter 9: Water Erosion and Deposition

Chapter Test

Question Number	Correct Answer	National Science Standard
1.	c.	D1 Grades 5–8
2.	h.	D1 Grades 5–8
3.	d.	D1 Grades 5–8
4.	j.	A1 Grades 5–12
5.	d.	D1 Grades 5–8
6.	h.	D1 Grades 5–8
7.	g.	A1 Grades 5–12

Standardized Test Practice

Question Number	Correct Answer
1	B
2	H
3	B
4	H
5	B
6	See page xxiv.
7	See page xxiv.

Chapter 10: Plate Tectonics

Chapter Test

Question Number	Correct Answer	National Science Standard
1.	c.	UCP3 Grades 5–12
2.	f.	D2 Grades 5–8
3.	d.	D2 Grades 5–8
4.	g.	D2 Grades 5–8
5.	c.	A2 Grades 5–12
6.	g.	D2 Grades 5–8
7.	b.	D2 Grades 5–8
8.	h.	D2 Grades 5–8
9.	b.	E2 Grades 5–8

Standardized Test Practice

Question Number	Correct Answer
1	D
2	J
3	B
4	G
5	B
6	F
7	D
8	See page xxiv.

Chapter 11: Earthquakes

Chapter Test

Question Number	Correct Answer	National Science Standard
1.	c.	F4 Grades 5–8
2.	h.	D1 Grades 5–12
3.	a.	E1 Grades 5–12
4.	j.	D1 Grades 5–8
5.	c.	F5 Grades 5–8
6.	g.	F3 Grades 5–8
7.	b.	D1 Grades 5–8
8.	j.	D1 Grades 5–8
9.	a.	D1 Grades 5–8

Standardized Test Practice

Question Number	Correct Answer
1	C
2	F
3	B
4	H
5	B
6	H
7	See page xxiv.
8	See page xxiv.

Chapter 12: Volcanoes

Chapter Test

Question Number	Correct Answer	National Science Standard
1.	a.	F2 Grades 5–8
2.	g.	D1 Grades 5–8
3.	d.	D1 Grades 5–8
4.	j.	UCP2 Grades 5–12
5.	b.	UCP2 Grades 5–12
6.	j.	UCP2 Grades 5–12
7.	b.	D1 Grades 5–8
8.	h.	D1 Grades 5–8
9.	b.	D1 Grades 5–8

Standardized Test Practice

Question Number	Correct Answer
1	C
2	G
3	C
4	J
5	B
6	G
7	D
8	See page xxiv.
9	See page xxiv.

Chapter 13: Clues to Earth's Past

Chapter Test

Question Number	Correct Answer	National Science Standard
1.	c.	D1 Grades 5–12
2.	f.	D2 Grades 5–8
3.	c.	B1 Grades 5–8
4.	j.	D2 Grades 5–8
5.	b.	A2 Grades 5–12

Standardized Test Practice

Question Number	Correct Answer
1	C
2	F
3	C
4	J
5	A
6	G
7	See page xxiv.

Chapter 14: Geologic Time

Chapter Test

Question Number	Correct Answer	National Science Standard
1.	d.	D1 Grades 5–12
2.	h.	D2 Grades 5–8
3.	b.	B1 Grades 5–8
4.	f.	D2 Grades 5–8
5.	b.	A2 Grades 5–12
6.	f.	D2 Grades 5–8

Standardized Test Practice

Question Number	Correct Answer
1	C
2	H
3	B
4	J
5	A
6	See page xxiv.
7	See page xxiv.

Chapter 15: Atmosphere

Chapter Test

Question Number	Correct Answer	National Science Standard
1.	d.	D2 Grades 5–8
2.	h.	D1 Grades 5–8
3.	b.	B3 Grades 5–8
4.	h.	F1 Grades 5–8
5.	a.	D1 Grades 5–8
6.	j.	D1 Grades 5–8
7.	c.	D1 Grades 5–8
8.	h.	D1 Grades 5–8
9.	c.	B3 Grades 5–8

Standardized Test Practice

Question Number	Correct Answer
1	A
2	F
3	B
4	J
5	C
6	J
7	C
8	See page xxv.

Chapter 16: Weather

Chapter Test

Question Number	Correct Answer	National Science Standard
1.	c.	D1 Grades 5–8
2.	h.	D1 Grades 5–8
3.	b.	D1 Grades 5–8
4.	f.	D1 Grades 5–8
5.	d.	A2 Grades 5–12
6.	j.	A2 Grades 5–12

Standardized Test Practice

Question Number	Correct Answer
1	C
2	G
3	D
4	H
5	A
6	F
7	B
8	F
9	See page xxv.

Chapter 17: Climate

Chapter Test

Question Number	Correct Answer	National Science Standard
1.	c.	C5 Grades 5–8
2.	g.	F3 Grades 5–8
3.	a.	F2 Grades 5–8
4.	j.	F2 Grades 5–8
5.	c.	F2 Grades 5–8
6.	j.	C5 Grades 5–8
7.	d.	F3 Grades 5–8
8.	g.	F2 Grades 5–8

Standardized Test Practice

Question Number	Correct Answer
1	A
2	G
3	A
4	J
5	C
6	H
7	D
8	H
9	See page xxv.

Chapter 18: Ocean Motion

Chapter Test

Question Number	Correct Answer	National Science Standard
1.	c.	D1 Grades 5–12
2.	g.	D1 Grades 5–12
3.	d.	B1 Grades 5–8
4.	g.	B1 Grades 5–8
5.	a.	D1 Grades 5–8
6.	h.	D3 Grades 5–8
7.	b.	A1 Grades 5–12
8.	j.	E2 Grades 5–12

Standardized Test Practice

Question Number	Correct Answer
1	C
2	H
3	B
4	H
5	C
6	See page xxv.
7	See page xxv.

Chapter 19: Oceanography

Chapter Test

Question Number	Correct Answer	National Science Standard
1.	d.	F4 Grades 5–12
2.	g.	C4 Grades 5–8
3.	d.	C4 Grades 5–8
4.	g.	D1 Grades 5–8
5.	b.	D1 Grades 5–8
6.	h.	C5 Grades 5–8
7.	d.	E1 Grades 5–12

Standardized Test Practice

Question Number	Correct Answer
1	B
2	H
3	B
4	H
5	B
6	G
7	See page xxv.
8	See page xxv.

Chapter 20: Our Impact on Land

Chapter Test

Question Number	Correct Answer	National Science Standard
1.	c.	F2 Grades 5–12
2.	j.	F2 Grades 5–12
3.	a.	F2 Grades 5–12
4.	j.	F2 Grades 5–12
5.	d.	A1 Grades 5–12
6.	f.	F2 Grades 5–12
7.	d.	F2 Grades 5–12

Standardized Test Practice

Question Number	Correct Answer
1	D
2	H
3	A
4	J
5	B
6	H
7	See page xxv.

Chapter 21: Our Impact on Water and Air

Chapter Test

Question Number	Correct Answer	National Science Standard
1.	c.	F2 Grades 5–8
2.	g.	F3 Grades 5–8
3.	a.	F2 Grades 5–8

Standardized Test Practice

Question Number	Correct Answer
1	A
2	H
3	A
4	J
5	B
6	H
7	D
8	See page xxv.
9	See page xxv.

Chapter 22: Exploring Space

Chapter Test

Question Number	Correct Answer	National Science Standard
1.	b.	E1 Grades 5–12
2.	h.	G3 Grades 5–8
3.	c.	D3 Grades 5–12
4.	g.	D3 Grades 5–12
5.	a.	E1 Grades 5–12
6.	h.	A1 Grades 5–12

Standardized Test Practice

Question Number	Correct Answer
1	C
2	F
3	A
4	H
5	B
6	J
7	A
8	See page xxv.

Chapter 23: The Sun-Earth-Moon System

Chapter Test

Question Number	Correct Answer	National Science Standard
1.	b.	D3 Grades 5–8
2.	g.	A2 Grades 5–12
3.	b.	E1 Grades 5–12
4.	f.	D1 Grades 5–8
5.	b.	D2 Grades 5–8
6.	g.	G1 Grades 5–12
7.	a.	D1 Grades 5–8
8.	h.	D2 Grades 5–8
9.	a.	D3 Grades 5–8
10.	h.	D3 Grades 5–8
11.	b.	D3 Grades 5–8

Standardized Test Practice

Question Number	Correct Answer
1	D
2	G
3	A
4	G
5	A
6	F
7	See page xxv.
8	See page xxv.

Chapter 24: The Solar System

Chapter Test

Question Number	Correct Answer	National Science Standard
1.	d.	D3 Grades 5–8
2.	f.	E1 Grades 5–12
3.	b.	A1 Grades 5–12
4.	g.	A1 Grades 5–12
5.	a.	A1 Grades 5–12
6.	j.	D3 Grades 5–12
7.	d.	D3 Grades 5–12
8.	h.	D3 Grades 5–12

Standardized Test Practice

Question Number	Correct Answer
1	C
2	F
3	A
4	H
5	B
6	H
7	See page xxv.
8	See page xxv.

Chapter 25: Stars and Galaxies

Chapter Test

Question Number	Correct Answer	National Science Standard
1.	c.	A1 Grades 5–12
2.	h.	A1 Grades 5–12
3.	b.	A1 Grades 5–12
4.	h.	D3 Grades 5–8
5.	d.	D3 Grades 5–8
6.	f.	A1 Grades 5–12

Standardized Test Practice

Question Number	Correct Answer
1	B
2	F
3	B
4	H
5	A
6	J
7	A
8	J
9	See page xxv.
10	See page xxv.

Answer Sheet

Name: Date:

Chapter:

Chapter Test

1	Ⓐ	Ⓑ	Ⓒ	Ⓓ	7	Ⓐ	Ⓑ	Ⓒ	Ⓓ
2	Ⓕ	Ⓖ	Ⓗ	Ⓙ	8	Ⓕ	Ⓖ	Ⓗ	Ⓙ
3	Ⓐ	Ⓑ	Ⓒ	Ⓓ	9	Ⓐ	Ⓑ	Ⓒ	Ⓓ
4	Ⓕ	Ⓖ	Ⓗ	Ⓙ	10	Ⓕ	Ⓖ	Ⓗ	Ⓙ
5	Ⓐ	Ⓑ	Ⓒ	Ⓓ	11	Ⓐ	Ⓑ	Ⓒ	Ⓓ
6	Ⓕ	Ⓖ	Ⓗ	Ⓙ	12	Ⓕ	Ⓖ	Ⓗ	Ⓙ

Standardized Test Practice

1	Ⓐ	Ⓑ	Ⓒ	Ⓓ	7	Ⓐ	Ⓑ	Ⓒ	Ⓓ
2	Ⓕ	Ⓖ	Ⓗ	Ⓙ	8	Ⓕ	Ⓖ	Ⓗ	Ⓙ
3	Ⓐ	Ⓑ	Ⓒ	Ⓓ	9	Ⓐ	Ⓑ	Ⓒ	Ⓓ
4	Ⓕ	Ⓖ	Ⓗ	Ⓙ	10	Ⓕ	Ⓖ	Ⓗ	Ⓙ
5	Ⓐ	Ⓑ	Ⓒ	Ⓓ	11	Ⓐ	Ⓑ	Ⓒ	Ⓓ
6	Ⓕ	Ⓖ	Ⓗ	Ⓙ	12	Ⓕ	Ⓖ	Ⓗ	Ⓙ

_____

_____

_____

_____

_____

_____

_____

_____

_____

Answers to Open-ended Questions

Chapter 1

7. Set up three different bulbs on the same parallel circuit. Turn all on at the same time. Record the approximate time that each burns out. Repeat the experiment.

Chapter 2

7. A physical property can be observed or measured without changing the sample's composition. A chemical property is the ability or inability to combine with another or change into new substances.

Chapter 5

7. Coal and natural gas are nonrenewable energy resources because they cannot be replaced by nature in a short period of time. The Sun, wind, and water are renewable resources that are recycled or replaced quickly by nature. Solar energy is used to heat homes, water, and to generate electricity. Windmills are used to convert wind into electrical energy. Running water is used to generate electricity.

Chapter 7

7. Mechanical weathering breaks rocks and minerals into smaller pieces but does not alter their chemical compositions. In chemical weathering, rocks and minerals undergo changes in chemical composition due to chemical reactions with agents such as water, acids, and oxygen. Mechanical weathering can increase the surface area of rocks and increase their exposure to agents of chemical weathering.

8. Horizon A — topsoil with large amounts of organic matter. Horizon B – subsoil with minerals leached from topsoil. Horizon C – weathered parent rock.

Chapter 8

6. Continental glaciers form over broad, continent-sized areas of land and usually spread outward from their centers. Valley glaciers are much smaller and form in mountainous regions. Both types erode and deposit rock and sediment.

7. Methods to decrease erosion include contour plowing (plow across slopes), cover crops (grow a new crop between harvests), terracing (create steps on a hillside), and no-till farming (plant in stubble).

Chapter 9

6. Young rivers flow over steep terrain. Waterfalls and rapids are common. Mature rivers meander across valleys. Old rivers flow through floodplains, empty into an ocean, and can build deltas. All carry bed, suspended, and dissolved load.

7. If acidic groundwater flows through pores or fractures in limestone, rock can dissolve and caves can form. Sinkholes form if the roof of a cave near Earth's surface collapses.

Chapter 10

8. Similar fossils and rocks on separate continents suggest that the continents were once connected.

Chapter 11

7. The differences in arrival times between P and S-waves can indicate the distance of a seismograph from an earthquake's epicenter. Information from three seismic stations enables scientists to plot the epicenter, the point at which three circles intersect, on a map.

8. The three types of faults are reverse, normal, and strike-slip. All are fractures in Earth's crust along which movement occurs. In reverse faults, rocks are pushed together by compression. In normal faults, rocks are pulled apart due to tension. Strike-slip faults form from horizontal shear stress.

Chapter 12

8. Shield — highly fluid, low-silica lava erupts and forms layer upon layer of volcanic rock. Composite— lava flows and eruptions of tephra; intermediate- or high-silica magmas are most common. Cinder cones — tephra is violently ejected and piles up; magma has high silica and gas content.

9. The Hawaiian Islands, in the middle of the Pacific Plate, formed as the plate drifted over a hot spot; basaltic eruptions built piles of volcanic rock. Most volcanoes form along plate margins where one plate is sinking beneath another. Partial melting is due to subduction.

Chapter 13

7. According to the principle of superposition, in undisturbed layers, the bottom layers are the oldest. Fossils in lower layers are older than those in the upper layers.

Chapter 14

6. Because the new butterfly mimics the monarch, monarch predators, such as birds, are deterred from eating the mimic because the monarch has an unpleasant taste. Hence, predators leave the mimic alone.

7. Cyanobacteria are photosynthetic, prokaryotic, single-celled organisms. In shallow waters, during the

Paleozoic Era, cyanobacteria produced layered mounded structures called stromatolites. The word *trilobite* is the common name for a group of extinct, marine arthropods that lived during the Paleozoic Era. Their exoskeletons had three sections. Dinosaurs were marine and land-dwelling reptiles that lived during the Mesozoic Era. Fossil teeth show that some were meat eaters, and others were plant eaters.

Chapter 15
8. Sailing ships depend upon wind to fill sails and move the ship, so it was important for them to travel in areas of the ocean where winds blow regularly and in known patterns. In the horse latitudes or doldrums, where there is little or no wind, a sailing ship risked floating aimlessly and cargo could spoil.

Chapter 16
9. Take temperature readings every half hour for a specific number of hours before, during, and after it rains. Repeat this procedure for at least three or more rainy days.

Chapter 17
9. Trees are a source for paper manufacturing and building materials. By cutting trees, habitats may be destroyed and less carbon dioxide removed from the atmosphere, which could lead to global warming.

Chapter 18
6. At the formation of Earth, the planet was much hotter than it is today. Countless volcanic eruptions released large amounts of water vapor over millions of years. As Earth cooled, the water vapor condensed to form rain that fell and filled ocean basins.

7. Density currents, caused by differences in the temperature and salinity of ocean water, move slowly in deep ocean waters. Surface currents, driven by wind, occur in the upper few hundred meters of the ocean and travel as fast as 100 km per day.

Chapter 19
7. The ocean basin changes when sediment is eroded or deposited. Over long periods of time, ocean basins change because of the movement of Earth's plates. For example, the Atlantic Ocean is becoming larger because of spreading at the Mid-Atlantic Ridge.

8. Common sources of ocean pollution include untreated sewage, runoff containing fertilizers and pesticides, oil spills, and discarded solid wastes. Ocean pollution can be reduced by treating sewage and by using chemicals wisely. People can participate in beach cleanups and in enforcing existing regulations.

Chapter 20
7. Starvation occurred because the attempt to restore the deer population failed to account for the impact of drastically reducing the populations of predators. Once predator populations decreased, the deer population exploded beyond the area's carrying capacity, their food became scarce, and deer died off.

Chapter 21
8. Read the label on the container for disposal information; follow the method detailed on the label; contact a local agency to find out about approved disposal regulations in your area.

9. Acid rain forms when pollutants such as sulfur oxides and nitrogen oxides enter the atmosphere and combine with water to form sulfuric and nitric acids. These acids then fall to Earth in precipitation. Acid rain can damage buildings and monuments by accelerating the rate of weathering. Acid rain can kill fish, damage plant foliage, and leach nutrients from soil.

Chapter 22
8. There was no cooperation during the race to the Moon. In recent years, the countries have cooperated in the *International Space Station,* in terms of funds, equipment, and crews.

Chapter 23
7. During a lunar eclipse, Earth blocks the Sun's light and casts an arc shaped shadow on the Moon.

8. Half of the Moon's surface is always illuminated by the Sun. A new moon is when the Moon is between Earth and the Sun. A full moon appears as a completely lit circle when Earth is between the Sun and the Moon. The Moon waxes from new moon to full moon, then wanes from full moon back to new moon.

Chapter 24
7. Scientists hypothesize that asteroids formed at the same time as Earth. If so, asteroids may reflect the structure and chemical composition of early Earth.

8. Mars is much farther from the Sun than is Earth.

Chapter 25
9. The star that appears brighter is closer to Earth.

10. If the universe is expanding, distant galaxies would exhibit a degree of red shift.

Introduction

What is in this book?

Welcome to the Student Edition of *Standardized Test Practice* for *Glencoe Earth Science*.

There are three distinct sections in this workbook:

- **Introduction: *Methods***

  This introduction provides you with methods to tackle test questions. Using the methods in this introduction, you will learn how to use the process of elimination, how to identify important information in the tests' graphs, charts, and tables, as well as other skills that can help you succeed on tests. Carefully study the methods in this introduction before you begin the test questions in this workbook.

  This workbook was written to accompany your textbook. For every chapter in your textbook, there are two types of tests in this workbook.

- **Chapter Test: *Content Mastery***

  For every chapter in the textbook, this workbook contains a Chapter Test. Each Chapter Test is made up of multiple-choice questions designed to assess your knowledge and understanding of the material in the corresponding chapter of the textbook.

- **Standardized Test Practice: *Test Preparation***

  For every chapter in the textbook, this workbook contains a corresponding Standardized Test Practice. The questions in this section are designed to prepare you for national science tests such as the TerraNova, the Iowa Tests of Basic Skills (ITBS), and the Stanford Achievement Test, Ninth Edition (SAT-9). The format of the questions found in these practice tests is very similar to the format of the questions found in the actual national science tests.

Task Regimen

A unique four-part **Task Regimen** and helpful **Test-Taking Tips** designed to maximize the benefits of using this workbook are presented in this section. Each of the four tasks is designed to help you identify challenges and improve your performance.

Each task has an assignment for you to do on your own at home and one to do in class. Often the homework and the in-class activities will be coordinated, so it is important that you concentrate on both equally.

TASK	At-Home Assignment	In-Class Assignment
Task 1	Using an answer key from the teacher, locate and review any questions you missed. Place a question mark beside any question you cannot figure out and bring it to class for discussion.	The teacher administers the test in a realistic test-taking environment.
Task 2	For each question you missed, find the pages in the textbook that cover the material and explain what specific information was needed to answer the question correctly. If you cannot find any helpful information in the textbook, write out three questions about the test question that you did not understand.	Work in a group to discuss any confusing questions and content areas. Then work through the confusing questions together.
Task 3	For every incorrect question, go through each answer choice and explain why it is correct or incorrect. Include any tips or hints you noticed that helped you eliminate choices. Place a question mark beside any question you cannot figure out and bring it to class for discussion.	Your teacher will lead a discussion for each question. Share your ideas and observations with the class. Keep notes of the discussion to help your review.
Task 4	Your teacher will provide you with a list of questions to work on. For each question, make observations and write down all of the information given in the test in the form of a graphic, a passage, or otherwise. Write the information directly onto the test.	Work in a group to discuss each question. Make sure to note the location in the textbook where helpful information was found.

Test-Taking Tips

Test-Taking Tips for Before the Test:

1. Be sure to get plenty of sleep the week before the test. A healthy amount of sleep is 8–9 hours every night.

2. The night before the test, try to do something relaxing but stimulating, such as playing a board game, exercising, or reading an enjoyable book. Cramming the night before the test often can hamper your memory and make you tired.

3. The morning of the test, eat a healthy breakfast with fresh foods that are high in protein and carbohydrates.

4. The morning of the test, clear your mind of any outside distractions so that you will be better able to focus on the test. If breaks are given during the test, use that time to relax and clear your mind.

Test-Taking Tips for During the Test:

1. Listen to and read all directions.

2. Be sure you understand the question before reading the answer choices. Then, make sure to read and consider **every** answer choice.

3. Remember to carefully consider all the information presented in the test's graphics.

4. If the test is timed, be sure to pace yourself.

5. Always choose an answer. By eliminating as many incorrect choices as possible, you will have a good chance at guessing correctly and obtaining more points.

DIRECTIONS

Choose the best answer choice for each of the following questions.

1. Taylor wanted to find out which brand of "C" batteries lasted the longest. He put one brand of "C" batteries into his radio. He put another brand of "C" batteries into a remote-controlled car. He timed how long each battery lasted before it ran out. His experiment could have been improved by _____.

   a. testing all the batteries in the same piece of equipment

   b. using "AAA" batteries in the car instead

   c. weighing the batteries before he started

   d. measuring how loud the radio could play

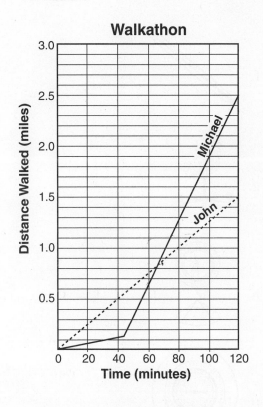

2. Information about scientific theory would most likely be found under which heading in a table of contents?

   f. Laws of Motion

   g. Doctor's Code of Ethics

   h. Repeated Tests Have Shown

   j. Mythology of Volcanoes

3. The graph shows the distance traveled by two different walkers during a two-hour walkathon. A reasonable hypothesis based on these data is that John _____.

   a. had walked farther than Michael after one hour

   b. walked faster and farther than Michael for the entire two hours

   c. is a better walker than Michael

   d. started faster than Michael did but walked fewer total miles

GO ON ▶

4. All of these pieces of technology are used to study weather EXCEPT _____.

f.

g.

h.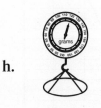

j.

Plant Growth After 2 Weeks

Seed Depth	Days to Sprout	Total Growth (cm)	Observations
0 cm			
1 cm			
2 cm			
3 cm			
4 cm			
5 cm			
6 cm			

5. The picture shows how a chart was set up for recording data from an experiment. Which of these is the most likely hypothesis tested in this experiment?

     a. Plants grow best when watered every day.

     b. Plants grow differently when seeds are planted at different depths.

     c. Seeds sprout faster when they are planted in the spring.

     d. All plants grow to their maximum height after two weeks.

Analyzing the results

F

Sharing the results

G

Testing a hypothesis

H

6. Marco needed to complete an experiment for a science presentation. Which is the order of the steps, from the first to the last, in the scientific method that Marco used?

     f. F, G, H

     g. H, F, G

     h. H, G, F

     j. G, H, F

DIRECTIONS

Read each question. Then, on your answer sheet, mark the answer choice that you think is best.

1 Scientists should repeat an experiment several times before making conclusions. It is important for them to do this in order to

   A use up all of their materials

   B make sure they get the same results every time

   C fill up a large data chart

   D give everyone a chance to participate in the experiment

2 A scientific experiment must have a control as part of the design so that

   F the experiment does not last too long

   G the experiment is done safely

   H there is something to compare the results to

   J the experiment will definitely get the right answer

Directions: This picture shows an experiment that explores how the Sun heats up different materials. The boxes in the picture are filled with air. Use the information in the picture to answer Numbers 3–4 below.

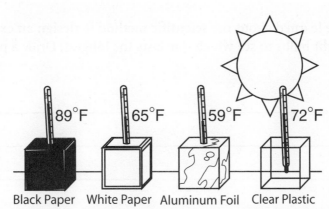

3 Which of the following would be the dependent variable in this experiment?

   A the temperature inside the boxes

   B the material covering the boxes

   C the Sun

   D the size of the boxes

4 A fifth box covered with red paper was added to the experiment. The thermometer coming out of this box had a reading of 66°F. Red paper seems to have an effect most similar to

   F black paper

   G white paper

   H aluminum foil

   J clear plastic

GO ON

Standardized Test Practice   Chapter 1 *The Nature of Science*

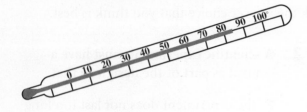

5   What information could be collected by using this piece of technology?

   A   time

   B   distance

   C   temperature

   D   volume

6   Scientists share their experimental procedures and results with each other so that

   F   they can be the first to discover something

   G   they can learn from each other and help each other

   H   they can get finished with their work faster

   J   no other scientist will do the same experiments they did

Directions: Read Number 7 below. Then, on the lines that follow, write your answer in complete sentences.

7   Use what you have learned about the scientific method to design an experiment that tests three brands of light bulbs to see which one lasts the longest. Draw a picture to help explain your experiment.

_____

_____

_____

_____

_____

_____

_____

_____

STOP

DIRECTIONS

Choose the best answer choice for each of the following questions.

1. Which of the following is a major characteristic of plasma?

   a. The electrons and ions have almost no attractive force to each other.

   b. The plasma state is denser than the solid state of most substances.

   c. The electrons and ions have a strong attractive force to each other.

   d. Electrons can sometimes escape the ion's electron cloud.

2. Under which heading in a table of contents would information about solids most likely be found?

   f. Water at 100°C

   g. Ions and Electrons

   h. Molecules in a Fixed Position

   j. Water at 0°C

Oxygen   Hydrogen   Carbon

3. Which of the following diagrams represents an unbonded element?

   a.

   b.

   c.

   d.

GO ON

4. Information about which of the following types of bonding would be most useful to a student studying the properties of solid gold?

  f. covalent

  g. ionic

  h. metallic

  j. hydrogen

5. When a large spoonful of sugar is stirred into the cup of hot water shown above, what happens to the sugar?

  a. The sugar reacts with the water.

  b. The sugar dissolves.

  c. The sugar disappears.

  d. The sugar boils.

6. When a container of water was slowly heated, the water in the container gradually disappeared. The most likely explanation for this is that the water molecules _____.

  f. were destroyed by the heat

  g. seeped into the walls of the container

  h. escaped into the air

  j. shrank until they disappeared

7. Saltwater can best be described as which of the following?

  a. a compound

  b. a solution

  c. an element

  d. a solid

STOP

DIRECTIONS

Read each question. Then, on your answer sheet, mark the answer choice that you think is best.

1 The state of matter that exhibits the strongest attractions between atoms and molecules is

  A solid

  B liquid

  C gas

  D plasma

2 Which of the following units could be used to measure the density of a substance?

  F meters per second

  G grams per second

  H meters per centimeter^3

  J grams per centimeter^3

3 A chemist weighed two different carbon atoms and found that one of them had a weight of 14 atomic mass units and the other had a weight of 12 atomic mass units. Which of the following is the reason for the difference in weight?

  A The two atoms had different numbers of protons.

  B The two atoms had different numbers of electrons.

  C The two atoms had different numbers of neutrons.

  D The two atoms were at different temperatures.

4 Which of the following has a positive charge?

  F proton

  G neutron

  H electron

  J molecule

GO ON

5 Which of the following does <u>not</u> have an electric charge?

  A neutron

  B electron

  C ion

  D proton

6 Mrs. Allen and her eighth-grade class are studying chemistry, but they are talking about cooking. Mrs. Allen tells her class that there is a compound that can be found as a solid, a liquid, or a gas in any kitchen. What compound can Mrs. Allen be describing?

  F air

  G metal

  H salt

  J water

Directions: Read Number 7 below. Then, on the lines that follow, write your answer in complete sentences.

7 Substances in nature have physical properties and chemical properties. What is the difference between a physical property and a chemical property?

_____

_____

_____

_____

_____

_____

_____

STOP

DIRECTIONS

Choose the best answer choice for each of the following questions.

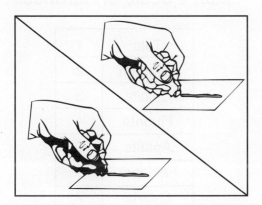

1. Which mineral property is being tested in the diagram above?

    a. cleavage

    b. hardness

    c. luster

    d. streak

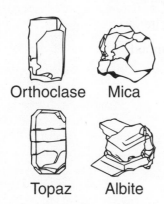

Orthoclase   Mica

Topaz   Albite

2. What property is being shown in all of the minerals above?

    f. metallic luster

    g. fracture

    h. cleavage

    j. streak

3. Titanium has all of these properties EXCEPT _____.

    a. durability

    b. low density

    c. crystalline structure

    d. non-toxicity

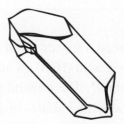

4. When conditions permit, many minerals form crystals with elaborate geometric patterns. The crystalline structure of quartz shown in the diagram above is due to _____.

    f. the types of chemical elements contained within the crystal

    g. the internal arrangement of atoms within the crystal

    h. how long ago the crystal formed

    j. the shape of the surrounding rocks where the crystal formed

GO ON ➡

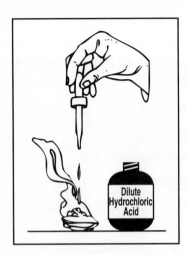

Moh's Scale of Hardness

Talc	1
Gypsum	2
Calcite	3
Fluorite	4
Apatite	5
Feldspar	6
Quartz	7
Topaz	8
Corundum	9
Diamond	10

5. Jamaal placed a few drops of dilute hydrochloric acid (HCl) on an unknown mineral sample. The mineral sample fizzed, producing bubbles of a gas. Most likely, the mineral sample was _____.

   a. calcite

   b. feldspar

   c. quartz

   d. mica

7. According to the chart, which of the following is the hardest mineral?

   a. quartz

   b. feldspar

   c. calcite

   d. diamond

6. Information about silicate would most likely be found under which heading in a table of contents?

   f. Moh's Scale of Hardness

   g. A Sparkling Wonder: The Hope Diamond

   h. Minerals Formed by Silicon and Oxygen

   j. Minerals That Taste Good!

STOP

DIRECTIONS

Read each question. Then, on your answer sheet, mark the answer choice that you think is best.

Mineral	Cleavage/ Fracture	Color	Streak	Luster
Biotite Mica	Cleavage thin	black to brown	Green	Glassy
Calcite	Cleavage rhombic	white to clear	White	Glassy
Fluorite	Cleavage 90°	purple to clear	White	Glassy
Galena	Cleavage 90°	silver to gray	Black	Metallic

1 Which of these could have a glassy luster, a white streak, a clear color, and cleavage at 90°?

A biotite mica

B calcite

C fluorite

D galena

2 In beach sand, quartz is the most abundant mineral because of its

F hardness

G streak

H cleavage

J luster

3 Most of the minerals found in rocks belong to a group that contains silicon, oxygen, and one or more metals. This group is called the

A carbonates

B ores

C oxides

D silicates

4 A mineral that contains a useful substance that can be mined for profit is called an ore. Which of the following may be classified as an ore?

F calcite ($CaCO_3$)

G halite ($NaCl$)

H hematite (Fe_2O_3)

J quartz (SiO_2)

GO ON

5   A mineral is a naturally occurring, inorganic, crystalline solid with a definite chemical composition. Which of the following is not a mineral?

A   calcite

B   coal

C   halite

D   talc

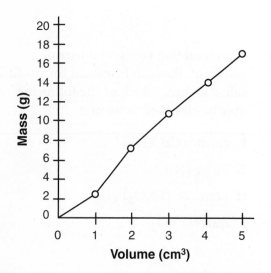

6   A student plotted the mass and volume of five different samples of the same mineral as shown on the graph above. She calculated the density using the formula D = M/V. The density she recorded was most likely measured in

F   grams

G   cubic centimeters

H   pounds per square inch

J   grams per cubic centimeter

Scale of Hardness

		Softest
1	Talc	
2	Gypsum	
3	Calcite	
4	Fluorite	
5	Apatite	
6	Orthoclase feldspar	
7	Quartz	
8	Topaz	
9	Corundum	
10	Diamond	Hardest

7   Which of these statements is true?

A   Apatite can scratch fluorite.

B   Diamond can be scratched by corundum.

C   Calcite can scratch quartz.

D   Topaz can be scratched by quartz.

8   Which statement provides the best description of the mineral property called streak?

F   Streak is the way a mineral reflects light from its surface.

G   Streak is the color of the powder left by a mineral when it is rubbed against a surface.

H   Streak is the ability of a mineral to resist being scratched.

J   Streak is the tendency of a mineral to easily break along smooth, definite surfaces.

STOP

DIRECTIONS

Choose the best answer choice for each of the following questions.

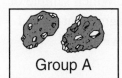
Group A

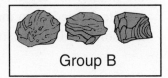
Group B

1. The rocks in Group A are different from the rocks in Group B because only the rocks in Group A have _____.

   a. foliated layers
   b. the mineral quartz
   c. visible crystals
   d. plant and animal remains

Detrital Sedimentary Rocks

Rock Name	Grain Size	Composition	Appearance
Conglomerate	larger than 0.2 cm	gravel, pebbles	rounded fragments
Sandstone	0.006 to 0.2 cm	sand	fine to coarse
Siltstone	0.004 to 0.006 cm	silt	very fine grain
Shale	smaller than 0.004 cm	clay	compact; splits easily

2. According to the table, a sedimentary rock with a grain size of 0.1 cm would have the name _____.

   f. conglomerate
   g. sandstone
   h. siltstone
   j. shale

3. Slate belongs to a group of rocks that have mineral grains lined up in parallel layers. According to this definition, which of these is slate?

   a.

   b.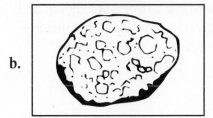

   c.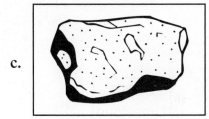

   d.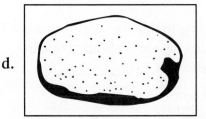

GO ON

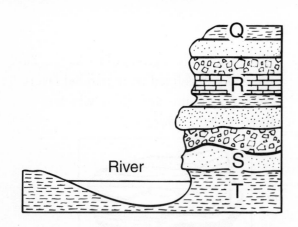

River

4. The diagram is a geologic cross-section of an area where a river has exposed a cliff of rock layers. According to the picture, which rock layer is the oldest?

   f. Q
   g. R
   h. S
   j. T

CaCO₃
Limestone

5. According to this chemical formula, all of the following elements are found in limestone EXCEPT _____.

   a. calcium
   b. carbon
   c. hydrogen
   d. oxygen

6. The size of crystals in igneous rock can be determined by how fast the magma cools and solidifies. The faster the magma cools, the smaller the crystals. Which sample of granite formed from magma that cooled and solidified at the slowest rate?

f.

g.

h.

j.

STOP

DIRECTIONS

Read each question. Then, on your answer sheet, mark the answer choice that you think is best.

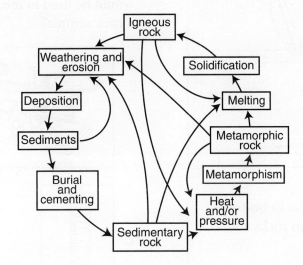

1   **Which statement is best supported by the information shown in the diagram?**

   A   Igneous rocks form by the melting and solidification of magma.

   B   Metamorphic rocks form by burial and cementing of sediments.

   C   Sedimentary rocks form by heat and pressure applied to other rocks.

   D   Igneous rocks form by weathering and erosion of other rocks.

---

2   Sedimentary rocks are classified according to grain size. Which of these is a measure of grain size?

   F   grams

   G   milliliters

   H   centimeters

   J   meters per second

3   Farina observed large crystals in a sample of granite. The large crystals in the sample were most likely formed by the

   A   compaction and cementation of sediments

   B   weathering and erosion of igneous rock

   C   slow cooling and solidification of magma

   D   application of heat and pressure from overlying rock layers

GO ON ➡

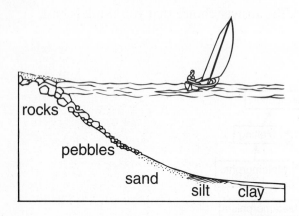

rocks

pebbles

sand

silt   clay

4   Silt and clay settle to the ocean bottom farther from the shore than rocks and pebbles because of their

  F   chemical composition

  G   spherical shape

  H   crystalline structure

  J   low density

5   Which statement accurately describes the process of metamorphism?

  A   Metamorphism is the changing of one type of rock into another as a result of heat and pressure.

  B   Metamorphism occurs only in active volcanoes.

  C   Erosion is the cause of all metamorphism.

  D   Metamorphism is the change that occurs in species over time.

6   Which of the following instruments would be used to measure the volume of a rock sample?

F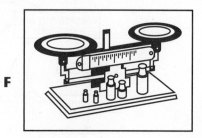

G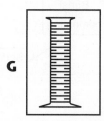

H

J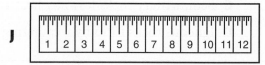

7   A geologist measured the density of a sample of basalt. The density recorded was most likely measured in

  A   grams

  B   grams per cubic centimeter

  C   pounds

  D   centimeters per pound

STOP

DIRECTIONS
Choose the best answer choice for each of the following questions.

1. All of the following are nonrenewable energy sources EXCEPT _____.
   a. coal
   b. geothermal energy
   c. natural gas
   d. petroleum oil

2. Information about oil and coal being used to heat homes would most likely be found under which heading in a table of contents?
   f. Nuclear Energy
   g. Renewable Resources
   h. Inexhaustible Resources
   j. Fossil Fuels

3. What type of energy production is occurring in the picture?
   a. hydroelectric energy
   b. solar energy
   c. geothermal energy
   d. biomass energy

SOLAR   WIND   HYDROELECTRIC

4. Which of these belongs with the group above?
   f. nonrenewable resources
   g. geothermal
   h. nuclear
   j. fossil fuel

GO ON ➡

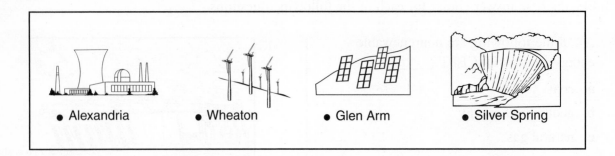

5. If the weather was cloudy for two weeks, the town whose energy source would be most affected is _____.

a. Wheaton

b. Silver Spring

c. Glen Arm

d. Alexandria

Some Mineral Resources and Their Uses

Mineral	Use
Hematite	Iron rods
Gypsum	Plaster casts
Saltpeter	Fertilizer
Feldspar	Pottery

6. According to this table, clay would most likely come from the mineral _____.

f. gypsum

g. feldspar

h. hematite

j. saltpeter

7. Which of the following is NOT a way to help conserve energy resources?

a. leave the windows slightly open in winter

b. turn off the lights when leaving the room

c. use solar power to heat your home

d. put extra insulation in the roof of your home

DIRECTIONS

Read each question. Then, on your answer sheet, mark the answer choice that you think is best.

1 Conservationists are hoping to replace oil with solar energy to heat downtown Millersville's office buildings. Which of the following will determine whether solar energy can be used for that purpose?

A the amount of oil that is used

B the kind of offices there are in downtown Millersville

C the number of cloudy days in Millersville

D the amount of oil reserves

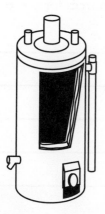

2 This water heater conserves energy because the insulating jacket

F provides a nonrenewable resource

G traps extra heat

H cools the water more quickly

J absorbs sunlight

3 Which of these would have the greatest effect on the energy supplied by a hydroelectric power plant?

A sand in the water

B the color of the water above the dam

C the temperature of the water above the dam

D the amount of water above the dam

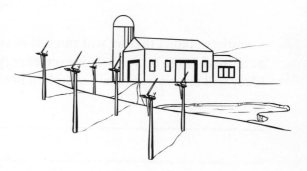

4 Which statement is accurate about the farm shown above?

F The energy for the farm is being provided by the Sun.

G The energy for the farm is being provided by the wind.

H The energy for the farm is being provided by the lake.

J The energy for the farm is being provided by fossil fuels.

GO ON ➡

5   Some regions can be very cloudy and rainy for most of the year. Which of the following would <u>not</u> be a good energy resource for those regions?

     A hydroelectric energy

     B oil

     C solar energy

     D nuclear energy

6   Which of the following is <u>not</u> an inexhaustible energy resource?

     F fossil fuel

     G solar energy

     H wind energy

     J geothermal energy

Directions: Read Number 7 below. Then, on the lines that follow, write your answer in complete sentences.

7   Scientists predict that we will run out of coal in 250 years. We also are expected to run out of natural gas in 60 years. However, energy resources that use the Sun, wind, or water most likely will always be available. Explain how we can use these sources for our energy needs.

_____

_____

_____

_____

_____

_____

_____

_____

_____

DIRECTIONS

Choose the best answer choice for each of the following questions.

1. The Hawaiian Islands are mountains that formed over a plate tectonic hot spot. Based on their method of formation, what kind of mountains are the Hawaiian Islands?

   a. fault-block mountains

   b. folded mountains

   c. upwarped mountains

   d. volcanic mountains

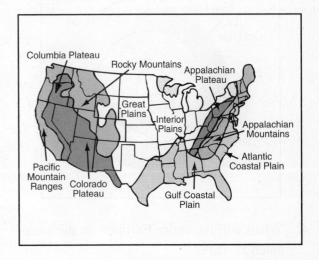

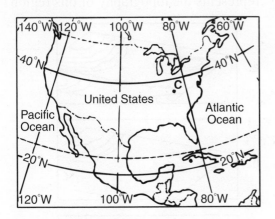

2. What is the approximate latitude and longitude of point C?

   f. 40°N, 80°W

   g. 35°N, 85°W

   h. 38°N, 83°W

   j. 83°N, 38°W

3. According to the map, which coast of the United States has no significant coastal plain?

   a. Atlantic coast

   b. Pacific coast

   c. Gulf coast

   d. West Texas coast

GO ON ➡

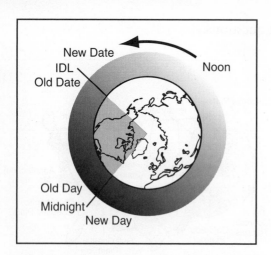

4. When will the entire Earth be on the same calendar date?

   f. on March 21, the vernal equinox

   g. on June 21, the summer solstice

   h. when it's midnight at the International Date Line.

   j. when it's noon at the International Date Line.

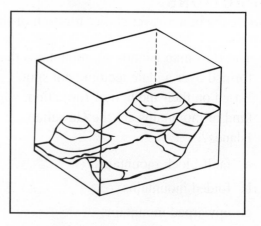

5. The diagram shows a model of a landscape region. Which of these maps best represents the topography of this region?

a.

b.

c.

d.

STOP

DIRECTIONS

Read each question. Then, on your answer sheet, mark the answer choice that you think is best.

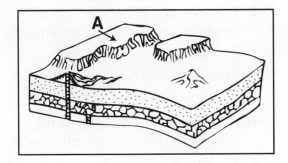

1 Structure A in the diagram above is a flat, raised area of land made up of nearly horizontal rocks that have been uplifted by forces within Earth. This structure is called a

A plain

B plateau

C mountain

D volcano

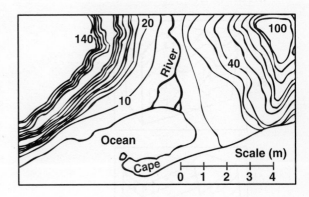

3 The elevation of the highest contour line shown on the topographic map above is

A 140 meters

B 150 meters

C 160 meters

D 180 meters

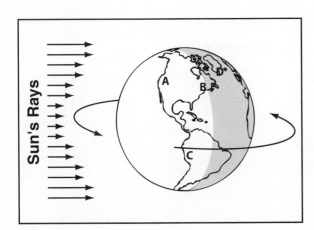

2 Which of these locations would enter the nighttime side of Earth next?

F A

G B

H C

J D

4 The Adirondack Mountains were formed when blocks of Earth's crust were pushed up by forces inside Earth. What type of mountains are the Adirondack Mountains?

F folded mountains

G upwarped mountains

H fault-block mountains

J volcanic mountains

GO ON

5   Which diagram represents folded mountains?

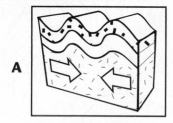

A

B

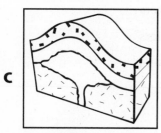

C

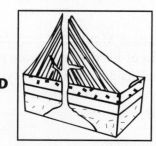

D

6   Which of these statements is true?

F   In a Mercator projection, lines of longitude are curved as they would be on a globe.

G   Mercator projections are used to produce maps of small areas.

H   A Mercator projection shows the changes in elevation of Earth's surface.

J   In a Mercator projection, areas near the poles are distorted.

7   Lines of latitude and longitude are used to form an imaginary grid system that allows people to locate any place on Earth accurately. The distance north or south of the equator and east or west of the prime meridian is measured in

A   degrees

B   kilometers

C   miles

D   nautical miles

STOP

DIRECTIONS

Choose the best answer for each of the following questions.

1. All of these are examples of mechanical weathering EXCEPT _____.

    a. ice wedging

    b. plant growth

    c. burrowing animals

    d. oxidation

2. Geologists in Petra, Jordan, are trying to protect an ancient city carved in the stone against the effects of weathering. Which of these questions should be answered first to determine how the city can be protected?

    f. How many tourists visit the site every year?

    g. Into which kind of stone is the ancient city carved?

    h. What are the average high and low temperatures in the region?

    j. Which type of soil exists in the region?

3. What is the reason many farmers use the method of terracing for growing crops?

    a. to reduce the effects of chemical weathering

    b. to increase the amount of erosion

    c. to increase the formation of gullies

    d. to reduce the amount of erosion

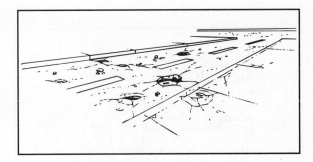

4. Cracks and potholes in the road are caused mainly by _____.

    f. oxidation

    g. acid rain

    h. ice wedging

    j. plant roots

OXIDATION	MECHANICAL WEATHERING	CHEMICAL WEATHERING

5. Which of these belongs with the group above?

    a. Horizon

    b. Soil profile

    c. Litter

    d. Ice wedging

GO ON ➡

6. Which of the following is a major characteristic of litter?

    f. decayed organic matter that has turned into a dark-colored material

    g. different layers of soil where the top layer is typically the darkest layer

    h. organic matter that might eventually decompose

    j. a mixture of rock, minerals, water, and decayed organic matter

7. Which of these is the main reason this land will most likely experience serious erosion in the future?

    a. the flowing stream

    b. cattle grazing

    c. the heat of the Sun

    d. the small number of trees

8. All of these are examples of human activities that cause serious soil erosion EXCEPT _____.

    f.

    g.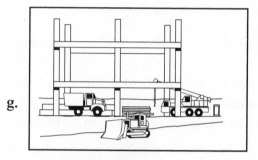

    h.

    j.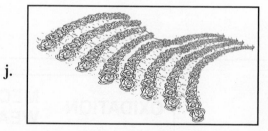

STOP

DIRECTIONS
Read each question. Then, on your answer sheet, mark the answer choice that you think is best.

1 Over thousands of years, caves are formed by a natural acid that dissolves rocks. This natural acid is called

   A carbonic

   B hydrochloric

   C hydroperoxide

   D stearic

2 Which of these farming methods does <u>not</u> help lessen soil erosion?

   F no-till farming

   G strip cropping

   H forest harvesting

   J terracing

3 As minerals in soil are dissolved by acids, they are carried from the A horizon to the B horizon by the process of

   A oxidation

   B mechanical erosion

   C leaching

   D humus formation

4 The rate of chemical weathering is less in Antarctica than in the rain forests of Brazil because of

   F the high amount of air moisture

   G the low temperatures

   H the heavy winds

   J the greater amount of organic materials in the soil

5 Josephine wants to determine in which horizon an unknown type of soil is found. She finds out through testing that it is dark and contains a lot of decomposed organic matter. She determines that this kind of soil is found in

   A the B horizon

   B the bedrock

   C topsoil

   D the C horizon

6 The World Heath Organization announced that the world's population is increasing at a very rapid rate. This increase in the world population will most likely also result in

   F an increase in soil erosion and destruction

   G a decrease in the eruption of volcanoes

   H an increase in soil buildup and construction

   J a decrease in chemical erosion

GO ON ➡

Standardized Test Practice *Chapter 7 Weathering and Soil*

Directions: Read Numbers 7–8 below. Then, on the lines that follow, write your answers in complete sentences.

7 Mechanical and chemical weathering are two different types of weathering. Discuss how they are different from and similar to each other. How do the two work together?

_____

_____

_____

_____

_____

_____

8 There are three different types of soil horizons: Horizon A, Horizon B, and Horizon C. Discuss the characterisics of each horizon.

_____

_____

_____

_____

_____

_____

_____

STOP

DIRECTIONS

Choose the best answer choice for each of the following questions.

1. All of these are major causes of erosion EXCEPT _____.

   a. water

   b. gravity

   c. sunlight

   d. wind

2. In a remote mountain town in California, a massive mudslide caused damage to homes. There were many eyewitnesses to the event. Which observation probably would NOT have contributed to the cause of the mudslide?

   f. There was record rainfall a few days before the mudslide occurred.

   g. There was very little vegetation on the mountain.

   h. High winds are common in the area.

   j. The soil was very dry.

3. Which of these processes is most responsible for the formation of sand dunes?

   a. water erosion

   b. volcanism

   c. wind erosion

   d. glaciation

4. Which of these soils will be most likely to experience the greatest amount of erosion?

   f.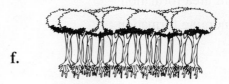

   g.

   h.

   j.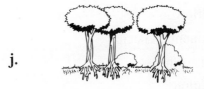

GO ON ➡

5. Thousands of years ago in the United States, which of these was LEAST likely to have occurred as a result of glaciation?

   a. sand dune formation

   b. plucking

   c. till area formation

   d. moraine formation

6. The greenhouse effect is slowly raising the average temperature of Earth's atmosphere. This will seriously affect the environment by _____.

   f. increasing the number of earthquakes

   g. increasing the melting of glaciers

   h. decreasing the number of mudslides

   j. decreasing the amount of wind erosion

SLUMP   CREEP   ROCKSLIDE

7. Which of these belongs with the group above?

   a. Mudflow

   b. Continental Glacier

   c. Sandstorm

   d. Deflation

8. Under which heading in a table of contents would the most information about loess be found?

   f. Erosion by Gravity

   g. Ice Depositing Sediment

   h. Erosion by Wind

   j. Deposition by Wind

9. Which of these is characteristic of creep?

   a. a single, large rock that slips down a slope

   b. loose materials that slip down slopes

   c. leaning vegetation

   d. a deposit of sediments

10. Nick is on a field trip with his science class. The teacher points to gouges that are in nearby bedrock. Nick knows that these gouges have resulted from which of the following?

   f. plucking and scouring

   g. moraine

   h. sand storms and rain storms

   j. mudflows

DIRECTIONS

Read each question. Then, on your answer sheet, mark the answer choice that you think is best.

1 The house in diagram A has a greater chance of being damaged by erosion than does the house in diagram B. Which of these would probably improve the safety of the home in diagram A?

A decreasing the amount of vegetation

B increasing the steepness of the slope

C decreasing the moisture of the soil

D increasing the amount of vegetation

2 What can you definitely conclude about the above sand dunes?

F Water erosion created them.

G The wind is moving them.

H The sand nearby is running out.

J They will remain for years.

3 Which of the following is <u>not</u> caused by glaciers?

A weathering of solid rock

B deposition of soil

C plucking of rocks

D dust storms

4 On which of the following mountain slopes would you expect the greatest amount of erosion to occur?

F

G

H

J

GO ON ➡

5   Which statement provides the best description of erosion?

    A It only is caused by water.

    B It is a slow and gradual process.

    C It only is caused by human activities.

    D It occurs very quickly in forests.

Directions: Read Numbers 6–7 below. Then, on the lines that follow, write your answers in complete sentences.

6   Continental and valley are the two different kinds of glaciers that exist on Earth's surface. Discuss the differences and similarities between them.

_____

_____

_____

_____

7   There are many things that a farmer can do to help decrease soil erosion. Discuss some of these methods.

_____

_____

_____

_____

STOP

DIRECTIONS

Choose the best answer choice for each of the following questions.

1. Florida is an area that has a lot of limestone and rainfall. These two factors could contribute to loss of physical property by _____ .

   a. increasing stalagmite formation

   b. increasing geyser formation

   c. increasing sink hole formation

   d. increasing water saturation of the soil

2. The most likely cause of sinkholes in areas like Florida and Kentucky is _____ .

   f. the water table being so close the Earth's surface that water flows out

   g. heated groundwater expanding underground until it shoots up

   h. groundwater dissolving limestone near Earth's surface

   j. groundwater flowing into a well near Earth's surface

RILL	GULLY	SHEET

3. Which of these belongs with the group above?

   a. Wells

   b. Mature

   c. Erosion

   d. Beach

4. All of these streams are examples of young streams EXCEPT _____ .

   f.

   g.

   h.

   j.

GO ON ➡

5. Under which heading in a table of contents would the most information about a barrier island be found?

     a. Coastal Currents

     b. Islands of Rock

     c. Sinkholes in the United States

     d. Protective Islands Formed by Sand

6. The picture shows four different types of soil on the side of a mountain. Various degrees of erosion take place for each section of soil. After a large rainfall, which soil would you expect to have the greatest amount of water erosion?

     f. Q

     g. R

     h. S

     j. T

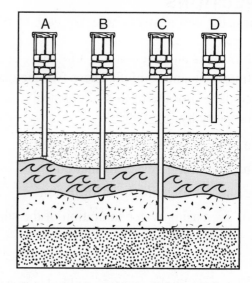

7. In the pictured well system, the well that would work best is _____.

     a. well A

     b. well B

     c. well C

     d. well D

CAREFUL: Hot Geysers in Area

8. Michelene is on a class trip in Yellowstone National Park. She sees this warning on a sign. The warning means that there are —

     f. areas of rock that are dissolved near the surface

     g. hot springs that erupt periodically

     h. rocks heated by magma

     j. hot meandering streams

STOP

Chapter 9 *Water Erosion and Deposition*   **Standardized Test Practice**

DIRECTIONS

Read each question. Then, on your answer sheet, mark the answer choice that you think is best.

1 Water flowing down the side of a slope that carries away plants and soil and creates a groove called a channel is an example of

A sheet erosion

B rill erosion

C gully erosion

D sedimentary erosion

2 The development of a mature stream is a process that takes many years. Which of the following criteria would define a stream as mature?

F quick water speed and lots of erosion

G curved shape and quick water speed

H curved shape and slow water speed

J quick water flowing in a narrow channel

3 Which of the following occurs when groundwater and molten rock are close to one another and to Earth's surface?

A cave

B hot spring

C cold spring

D sink hole

4 Which of the following is <u>not</u> a result of water erosion and deposition?

F barrier island

G sandbar

H coral reef

J spit

5 Which of the following is true about beaches?

A They are always composed of grains of quartz.

B They are short-term land features.

C They are permanent land features.

D They are not susceptible to erosion.

GO ON

Standardized Test Practice   Chapter 9 *Water Erosion and Deposition*

Directions: Read Number 6 below. Then, on the lines that follow, write your answers in complete sentences.

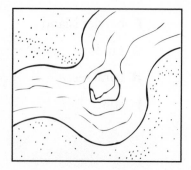 

6   River formation is a process that takes many, many years. Discuss the different stages of river development. How are they similar? How are they different?

_____

_____

_____

_____

_____

_____

_____

7   Explain how groundwater can form caves and sinkholes.

_____

_____

_____

_____

_____

DIRECTIONS

Choose the best answer choice for each of the following questions.

Movement of the North American Continent: 1998–2001

Year	Distance Moved from First Measurement
1998	5.2
1999	10.4
2000	15.6
2001	?

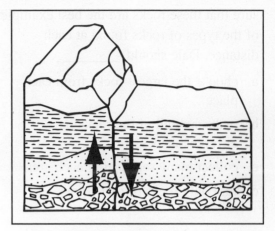

1. Scientists studying plate tectonics compiled the chart above showing the distance that the North American continent moves from year to year. Based on this information, how far will the continent have moved from the first measurement in the year 2001?

   a. 10.4 cm
   b. 15.6 cm
   c. 20.8 cm
   d. 26.0 cm

2. Which of the following is NOT evidence used to support the theory that Earth's continents were once connected?

   f. The continents can support animal life.
   g. Similar geological features are found on widely separated continents.
   h. The coastlines of some continents fit together like puzzle pieces.
   j. Similar fossils are found on widely separated continents.

3. Which process is taking place in the picture above?

   a. soil erosion
   b. river flooding
   c. iceberg creation
   d. mountain building

4. The Mariana Islands in the Pacific Ocean were formed by volcanic action. Which of the following is most likely true?

   f. There are glaciers near the Mariana Islands.
   g. Tectonic plates collide near the Mariana Islands.
   h. The Mariana Islands are larger than most islands.
   j. The Mariana Islands are uninhabited.

GO ON

5. Dale collected a rock at several different distances from a fault line. In order to be sure that these rocks are the best examples of the types of rocks found at each distance, Dale should _____.

   a. choose the largest rocks from each place

   b. make sure all of the rocks have different shapes

   c. collect many rocks from each area

   d. find only rocks of one color

6. The most likely cause of earthquake activity on the West Coast of the United States is _____.

   f. landslides from coastal mountains

   g. the slipping of tectonic plates

   h. tidal effects from the Pacific Ocean

   j. seasonal temperature changes

7. Under which of the following headings in a table of contents would the most information about Pangaea be found?

   a. How to Clean and Prepare Fossil Samples

   b. Alfred Wegener and Continental Drift

   c. The Movement of Glaciers

   d. All You Need to Know About the Asthenosphere

8. Which of the following is LEAST likely to result from seafloor spreading?

   f. magma flowing upward toward cracks

   g. creation of mid-ocean ridges

   h. a reversal in the magnetic fields of the north and south poles

   j. magma cooling and forming solid, new seafloor

9. Which kind of scientist would most likely use a graph titled "Magnitude of some Earthquakes"?

   a. biochemist

   b. geologist

   c. toxicologist

   d. physicist

STOP

DIRECTIONS

Read each question. Then, on your answer sheet, mark the answer choice that you think is best.

1 When tectonic plates collide, molten rock from beneath the crust of the earth is sometimes forced up through the surface. When this occurs, it is called

A a mountain

B an earthquake

C a rift

D a volcano

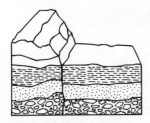

2 Which of the following is <u>not</u> caused by plate tectonics?

F earthquakes

G volcanoes

H mountain building

J tidal cycles

3 A scientist measured the distance moved by a tectonic plate over the course of a year. The distance would best be recorded in what units?

A kilometers

B centimeters

C liters

D miles

4 Why is it hazardous to build a house on a fault line?

F The house will be too costly to maintain.

G The house may be destroyed by an earthquake.

H The house will be difficult to heat.

J The house will be too small.

5 The gradual movement of the continents across the surface of Earth is best explained by which of the following?

A gravitational attraction

B plate tectonics

C solar radiation

D the greenhouse effect

GO ON

6 Some mountains are formed by the collision of two tectonic plates. Which of the diagrams below shows a situation that would result in the formation of such mountains?

F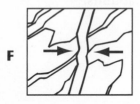

G

H

J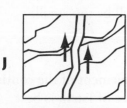

7 Which of the following diagrams represents a fault line?

A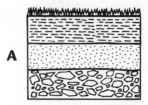

B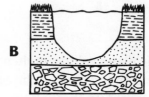

C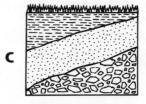

D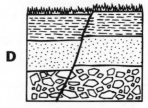

Directions: Read Number 8 below. Then, on the lines that follow, write your answer in complete sentences.

8 Similar fossils and rock formations have been found in western Africa and eastern South America. Explain how this information can be used to support the theory of plate tectonics.

_____

_____

_____

STOP

DIRECTIONS

Choose the best answer choice for each of the following questions.

1. The San Andreas Fault cuts through California. This fault could affect human health most by _____.

   a. decreasing the oxygen levels in the atmosphere

   b. decreasing the amount of erosion

   c. increasing the number of earthquakes

   d. increasing the number of rainstorms

2. Which rope is moving most like seismic waves?

    f.

   g.
   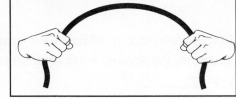

   h.

   j.

3. Earthquakes create all of these types of waves EXCEPT _____.

   a. tertiary

   b. secondary

   c. primary

   d. surface

4. When tectonic plates move, they place a lot of stress on rocks, sometimes causing them to break. Why are earthquakes caused by rocks breaking?

   f. the tectonic plates keep moving

   g. the ground sinks in between tectonic plates

   h. the tectonic plates create strong surface waves

   j. the breaking rocks produce vibrations

GO ON ➡

5. Which has been the greatest benefit of studying and measuring seismic waves?

   a. prevention of all earthquakes worldwide

   b. prediction of earthquakes

   c. mapping of Earth's internal structure

   d. understanding tsunamis

6. If a major earthquake occurred in a populated inland area far from the shore, which of these would be LEAST likely to result?

   f. damage to buildings and structures

   g. tsunamis

   h. loss of human lives

   j. landslides

7. Buildings in areas where earthquakes happen frequently need to be seismically safe. Which of the following describes how a building in these areas should be built?

   a. Buildings should be built so they will stand rigidly and not be able to sway.

   b. Buildings should have rubber moorings so they will sway instead of collapsing.

   c. Buildings should be built without reinforcing rods.

   d. Buildings should be built only on epicenters.

8. When enough force is applied to rocks, they may break apart. The surface of these broken rocks is called a _____.

   f. tsunami

   g. earthquake

   h. seismic wave

   j. fault

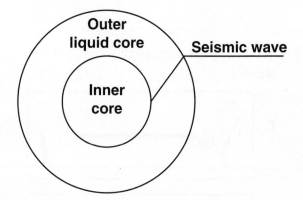

9. In this cross-section of Earth's internal structure, the seismic wave represented is a _____.

   a. primary wave

   b. secondary wave

   c. surface wave

   d. Richter wave

STOP

DIRECTIONS

Read each question. Then, on your answer sheet, mark the answer choice that you think is best.

1 Which is <u>not</u> an example of a type of fault?

   A strike-slip

   B reverse

   C vertical

   D normal

2 What is true about surface waves?

   F They cause the majority of the destruction associated with earthquakes.

   G They are the fastest moving waves associated with earthquakes.

   H They do not pass through liquid.

   J They do not slow down when entering a denser layer of Earth.

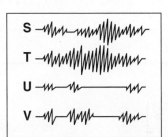

3 Four recent earthquakes in California were recorded with this seismograph. Which of these earthquakes do you think most likely caused the largest change to the landscape?

   A S

   B T

   C U

   D V

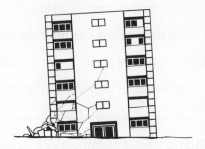

4 The Northridge, California, earthquake in 1994 caused this building to sink and then collapse. Which process was responsible for weakening the soil underneath the building?

   F sedimentation

   G weathering

   H liquefaction

   J seismosis

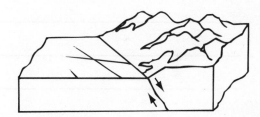

5 Which is an accurate statement about this fault?

   A Tension forces pull the rocks apart.

   B It is the result of compressive forces.

   C It is the result of shear force.

   D It probably will not cause an earthquake.

GO ON ➡

6 Which best describes earthquake activity?

    F Earthquakes are rare events.

    G The majority of earthquakes are destructive.

    H Earthquakes occur every day all over the world.

    J Earthquakes only can occur once at a single fault.

Directions: Read Numbers 7–8 below. Then, on the lines that follow, write your answers in complete sentences.

7 Seismologists locate an earthquake's epicenter based on the different speeds of seismic waves. Discuss in detail how they are able to locate an earthquake's epicenter.

_____

_____

_____

_____

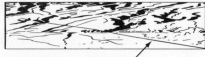

San Andreas Fault Line

8 Discuss the similarities and differences between the three different kinds of faults.

_____

_____

_____

STOP

DIRECTIONS

Choose the best answer choice for each of the following questions.

1. A volcanic eruption is a dramatic and powerful event. A volcanic eruption can positively affect the environment by _____.

   a. increasing the number of islands
   b. increasing the amount of acid rain
   c. decreasing plant and animal life
   d. decreasing the number of inhabited villages

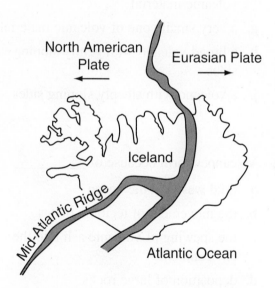

2. The most likely cause of volcanic activity on the island of Iceland is _____.

   f. the strength of the Atlantic Ocean's currents
   g. the pulling apart of the tectonic plates
   h. the colliding of the tectonic plates
   j. a hot spot under a tectonic plate

3. All of the following are kinds of volcanoes EXCEPT _____.

   a. cinder cone
   b. shield
   c. composite
   d. magmatic

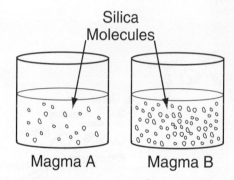

4. Silica often becomes trapped in magma. What kind of eruption do you think Magma B will most likely cause?

   f. basaltic
   g. quietly flowing
   h. non-explosive
   j. explosive and violent

GO ON ➡

5. The most likely cause of the slow movement of magma toward Earth's surface is that _____.

   a. magma is more dense than the rock around it

   b. magma is less dense than the rock around it

   c. magma is hotter than the rock around it

   d. magma is cooler than the rock around it

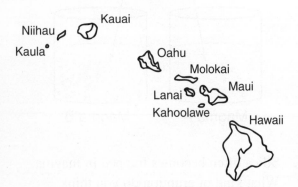

6. The Hawaiian Islands were formed by volcanic activity. A reasonable hypothesis based on this information is that in the distant future _____.

   f. the islands will sink

   g. the islands will become smaller

   h. there will be no more volcanic activity

   j. there will be more islands

7. Under which heading in a table of contents would the most information about tephras be found?

   a. Shield Volcanoes

   b. Cinder-Cone Volcanoes

   c. Batholiths

   d. Calderas

8. Which of these best describes a shield volcano?

   f. a small crack or fissure erupting volcanic material

   g. a very small cone of volcanic material

   h. a broad volcano with gently sloping sides

   j. a volcano with steeply sloping sides

9. Volcanoes form because of _____.

   a. tidal waves in the ocean

   b. the movement of tectonic plates

   c. the spewing of volcanic ash into the environment

   d. deposition of large rocks

STOP

DIRECTIONS

Read each question. Then, on your answer sheet, mark the answer choice that you think is best.

1 Magma is pushed upwards from the core of Earth and flows through openings called

   A craters

   B volcanic holes

   C vents

   D hot spot

2 The eruption of the Soufriere Hills volcano on the island of Montserrat was extremely explosive and violent. What two materials in the magma most contributed to this explosive eruption?

   F water vapor and calcium

   G silica and trapped gases

   H sulfur and igneous rock

   J silica and basalt

3 What is true about basaltic magma?

   A It is silica-rich.

   B It causes explosive eruptions.

   C It is not silica-rich.

   D It is very thick.

4 Which of the following is most likely <u>not</u> a result of volcanic activity?

   F batholith

   G horizontal sills

   H vertical dike

   J water erosion on beach

5 Which statement about lava flows is accurate?

   A They always move rapidly.

   B They destroy everything in their paths.

   C They cool down and change into magma.

   D They are not very damaging to the environment.

6 Which of the following type of volcano forms when lava cools in the air, hardening into a material called tephra?

   F shield

   G cinder cone

   H component

   J composite

GO ON ▶

7   Which of the following is <u>not</u> a type of lava?

    A basaltic

    B andesitic

    C granitic

    D composite

Directions: Read Numbers 8–9 below. Then, on the lines that follow, write your answers in complete sentences.

8   There are three basic types of volcanoes: shield volcanoes, cinder cone volcanoes, and composite volcanoes. Discuss how each is formed. How are their lava eruptions different? How is the composition of their lava different?

_____

_____

_____

_____

9   The Hawaiian Islands in the Pacific Ocean were created by a volcanic hot spot. Discuss how hot spot volcanoes are different from volcanoes that are formed as a result of the movement of Earth's plates, such as those in the Antilles.

_____

_____

_____

_____

_____

_____

STOP

DIRECTIONS

Choose the best answer choice for each of the following questions.

Ages of Fossils Found at Site X

Fossil	Age (years)
Q	10,000
R	20,000
S	15,000
T	5,000
U	10,000

1. The chart above shows the ages of some fossils found at a particular archeological site. Which of the following graphs best represents these data?

a.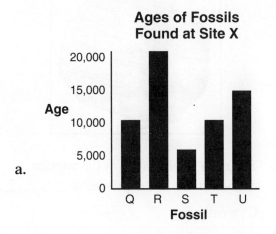

c.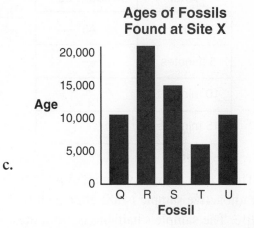

b.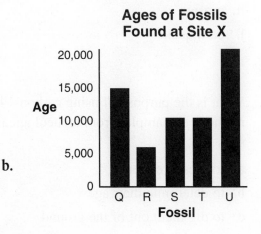

d.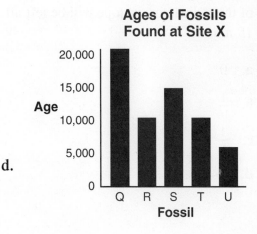

GO ON ➤

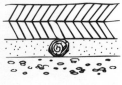
Q

R

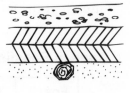
S

T

2. Which is the order, from first to last, of the formation of a fossil?

   f. R, T, Q, S

   g. Q, R, S, T

   h. Q, S, T, R

   j. S, Q, R, T

After	Amount Left
0	All
5 minutes	$\frac{1}{2}$
10 minutes	$\frac{1}{4}$
15 minutes	?

3. These data show how much of a radioactive sample is left after each half-life. The sample's half-life is 5 minutes. If everything remains the same, what fraction of the radioactive isotope will be left after 15 minutes?

   a. 0

   b. $\frac{1}{16}$

   c. $\frac{1}{8}$

   d. $\frac{1}{3}$

4. The most likely cause of the angular unconformity in the picture is _____.

   f. weathering

   g. radioactive decay

   h. erosion

   j. earthquake

5. What is the purpose of using carbon-14 methods on samples from archeological sites?

   a. to preserve them

   b. to determine their age

   c. to dig them out of the ground

   d. to clean them

DIRECTIONS

Read each question. Then, on your answer sheet, mark the answer choice that you think is best.

1 Which of the following would <u>not</u> be called an original remains fossil?

A a plant fossil caught in a tar pit

B a fly caught in amber

C a dinosaur tooth

D a frozen woolly mammoth

2 Which of these pictures is an example of a trace fossil?

F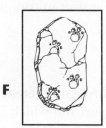

G

H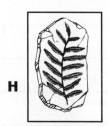

J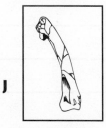

3 Sediments increase the chance that a dead organism will turn into a fossil by

A keeping it afloat

B helping it be decomposed by bacteria

C protecting it from being decomposed

D giving it fertilizer

4 Which diagram represents alpha decay?

F $$^{234}_{90}\text{Th} \longrightarrow ^{234}_{91}\text{Pa} + ^{0}_{-1}\text{e}$$

G $$2\text{H}_2\text{O} \longrightarrow 2\text{H}_2 + \text{O}_2$$

H $$\text{O}_2 + \text{C}_6\text{H}_{12}\text{O}_6 \longrightarrow \text{H}_2\text{O} + \text{CO}_2$$

J $$^{238}_{92}\text{U} \longrightarrow ^{234}_{90}\text{Th} + ^{4}_{2}\text{He}$$

GO ON ➡

5 An archeologist uses dating methods to determine the age of a fossil. The age she writes in her chart was most likely measured in

A years

B light-years

C minutes

D days

6 Which of these sentences gives the best definition of half-life?

F Half-life is the amount of time it takes for an animal to reach middle age.

G Half-life is the amount of time it takes for half of a sample of atoms to decay.

H After two half-lives, all of the atoms in a sample are gone.

J Half-life is when a chemical reaction is half over.

Directions: Read Number 7 below. Then, on the lines that follow, write your answer in complete sentences.

7 Max and Gladys are digging at an archeological site. As they dig down through different layers of sediment, they find all kinds of fossils. Explain how they can figure out which fossils are older and which are younger, using the term "superposition" in your answer. Draw a diagram as part of your explanation.

_____

_____

_____

_____

_____

_____

_____

_____

STOP

DIRECTIONS

Choose the best answer choice for each of the following questions.

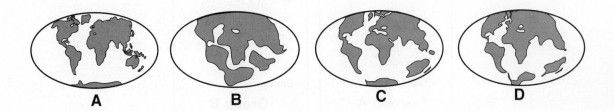

A   **B**   **C**   **D**

1. Which of the following lists the the contintents' positions from earliest to latest?

   a. A, B, C, D

   b. D, C, B, A

   c. C, A, B, D

   d. B, D, C, A

---

2. In a table of contents, under which heading would you find the most information about dinosaurs?

   f. Proterozoic Era

   g. Paleozoic Era

   h. Mesozoic Era

   j. Cenozoic Era

3. What characteristic will help the deer be successful in this habitat?

   a. their stripes

   b. their long necks

   c. their dark color

   d. their small tails

GO ON ➡

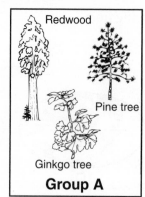

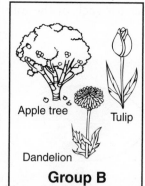

Group A   **Group B**

4. The plants in Group A are different from the plants in Group B because only the plants in Group B have _____.

    f. flowers

    g. pine cones

    h. branches

    j. roots

5. In general, having scaly skin benefits reptiles most by _____.

    a. allowing them to swim easily

    b. keeping them from losing water

    c. helping them to fly to high tree branches

    d. keeping them warm during cooler seasons

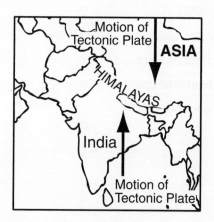

6. Which of these processes most contributed to the formation of the Himalayas?

    f. collision of continents

    g. melting of glaciers

    h. erosion by wind and water

    j. landslides from monsoons

STOP

DIRECTIONS

Read each question. Then, on your answer sheet, mark the answer choice that you think is best.

1 Which of these is a warm-blooded animal?

  A snake

  B tropical fish

  C bird

  D earthworm

2 Which sentence gives the best description of natural selection?

  F Natural selection is how animals choose the habitat they will live in.

  G Natural selection is when humans make national parks.

  H Natural selection is when animals that are better suited to an environment survive more successfully.

  J Natural selection is how animals change their behavior and their physical appearance in order to get more food.

3 About 66 million years ago, something happened on Earth that killed off many species of plants and animals. This phenomenon is called

  A continental drift

  B mass extinction

  C an eon

  D photosynthesis

4 Several billion years ago, cyanobacteria began photosynthesizing. What did this add to Earth's atmosphere?

  F water

  G carbon dioxide

  H sunlight

  J oxygen

5 Which of the following is <u>not</u> a geological time period?

  A Pangaea Era

  B Cenozoic Era

  C Mesozoic Era

  D Paleozoic Era

GO ON

Directions: Read Numbers 6–7 below. Then, on the lines that follow, write your answers in complete sentences.

6 Monarch butterflies are unpleasant tasting to animals like frogs. Another species of butterfly evolved with wings that look similar to the monarch butterfly's wings. Explain how this will affect the survival of the new butterfly.

_____

_____

_____

_____

_____

_____

7 Over the course of Earth's history, many different organisms have existed, such as cyanobacteria, trilobites, and dinosaurs. Pick one organism, note the era(s) in which it existed, and describe its main characteristics.

_____

_____

_____

_____

_____

_____

STOP

DIRECTIONS

Choose the best answer choice for each of the following questions.

1. Earth's atmosphere changed over time and eventually was able to support plant life. Which of these is the most likely cause of the change?

   a. Increased volcanic activity produced a lot of nitrogen and carbon dioxide gas.

   b. Gases from outer space entered Earth's atmosphere.

   c. Sunlight caused oxygen gas to form in the atmosphere.

   d. The ozone layer formed, protecting plants from ultraviolet radiation.

2. In which one of Earth's systems are these pictures taking place?

   f. mesosphere

   g. stratosphere

   h. hydrosphere

   j. thermosphere

3. What type of energy transfer occurs when the heat in the sand transfers to the person's feet?

   a. convection

   b. conduction

   c. radiation

   d. kinetic

4. Which of these characteristics would be the most important in a sunscreen?

   f. the brand name

   g. the types of moisturizing ingredients for the skin

   h. the amount of protection from ultraviolet radiation

   j. the quality of the perfumes added

GO ON

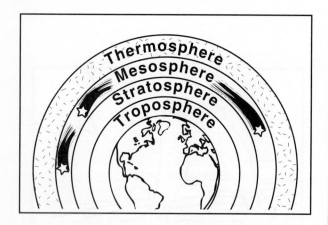

7. Which of the following is NOT a characteristic of the troposphere?

   a. Contains a high level of water vapor

   b. Contains a high level of atmospheric gases

   c. Contains a high level of ozone

   d. Extends from the surface of Earth up to about 10 kilometers

5. In the thermosphere, there is a layer called the ionosphere that can help radio waves travel. The ionosphere is made up of _____.

   a. electrically charged particles

   b. prevailing easterlies

   c. ultraviolet radiation from the sun

   d. carbon dioxide gas from cars

8. Which of the following causes cold air to move from the land to the water?

   f. sea breeze

   g. Coriolis effect

   h. land breeze

   j. trade winds

6. Which type of wind generally moves from the southwest to the northeast in the northern hemisphere?

   f. polar easterlies

   g. jet stream

   h. sea breeze

   j. prevailing westerlies

RADIATION   CONVECTION   CONDUCTION

9. Which of these can be associated with the group above?

   a. ozone

   b. ultraviolet

   c. heat

   d. thermosphere

DIRECTIONS

Read each question. Then, on your answer sheet, mark the answer choice that you think is best.

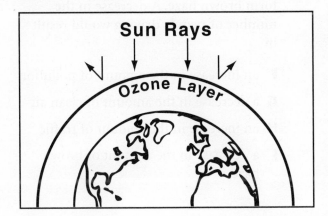

1 Plants and animals thrived on Earth after the ozone layer was formed. It protects the Earth from

  A solar radiation

  B meteor showers

  C acid rain

  D volcanic gas

2 Seth's teacher explained that the hydrosphere consists of all the water on Earth's surface. Which of the following is a part of the hydrosphere?

  F snow

  G wind

  H sunlight

  J soil

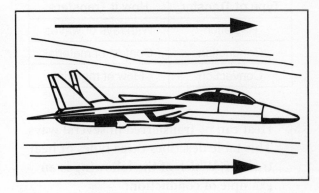

3 Jet streams enable pilots to reach their destinations faster. Which of these must be true in order for this to happen?

  A There can be no clouds or rain in the jet stream.

  B The wind and plane have to be moving in the same direction.

  C The plane has to be flying at altitudes lower than the clouds.

  D The plane has to be flying in a windy season.

4 Some people need special products to prevent them from getting sunburned. These products can do this by

  F changing the skin into a darker color

  G absorbing sunlight into the skin

  H reflecting sunshine from the skin like a mirror

  J preventing harmful UV rays from entering the skin

GO ON ➡

Standardized Test Practice   Chapter 15 *Atmosphere*

Heat Transfer

Type of Transfer	How It Transfers
Radiation	With rays or waves
Conduction	Contact of material
Convection	Flow of material

5   Heat can be transferred in several ways. This table describes three types of heat transfer. Which of the following is an example of conduction?

   A   sun shining on a metal chair

   B   fire heating a room

   C   a metal pan burning a hand

   D   hair dryer blowing hair

6   Car exhaust combines with the air to form brown haze. A decrease in the number of people driving would result in

   F   an increase in the amount of pollution

   G   a decrease in the amount of clean air

   H   an increase in the amount of traffic

   J   a decrease in the amount of brown haze

7   The troposphere is the layer of the atmosphere closest to Earth's surface. Which of these would you expect to find in the troposphere?

   A   a shooting star

   B   extremely high temperatures

   C   clouds and rain

   D   the ionosphere

Directions: Read Number 8 below. Then, on the lines that follow, write your answer in complete sentences.

8   Some areas of Earth receive much more wind than other areas. Early traders used sailboats to travel across the ocean. Explain why it was necessary for them to learn which areas had wind and which areas didn't.

_____

_____

_____

_____

STOP

DIRECTIONS

Choose the best answer choice for each of the following questions.

W   X

Y   Z

1. What is the correct sequence for the formation of a cold front?

   a. W, Y, X, Z

   b. Y, W, X, Z

   c. Y, Z, X, W

   d. Z, X, W, Y

2. Which of these facts best explains why warmer air causes an increase in humidity and cooler air causes a decrease in humidity?

   f. Sunlight evaporates moisture.

   g. Saturated air cannot hold any more moisture.

   h. Cool air causes water molecules to join and condense.

   j. The dew point changes with the amount of moisture in the air.

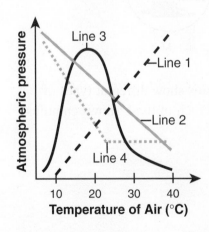

3. Which of the lines above correctly represents the relationship of temperature to atmospheric pressure?

   a. 1

   b. 2

   c. 3

   d. 4

GO ON

A

B

C

D

4. The pictures show different types of clouds. Which of these shows cumulus clouds?

   f. A

   g. B

   h. C

   j. D

5. Severe weather can be very dangerous. What does it mean when the National Weather Service issues a tornado warning?

   a. There is a small chance of a tornado forming.

   b. A tornado is in a nearby area, but it is not severe enough to cause damage.

   c. A tornado might occur the next day.

   d. A tornado has been sighted and immediate action should be taken.

Precipitation Amounts

Month	Precipitation (cm)
March	10.63
April	11.47
May	14.68
June	9.32
July	5.87
August	4.99

6. According to the chart, which month had the LEAST precipitation?

   f. March

   g. May

   h. June

   j. August

STOP

DIRECTIONS

Read each question. Then, on your answer sheet, mark the answer choice that you think is best.

Thunder and Lightning Chain of Events

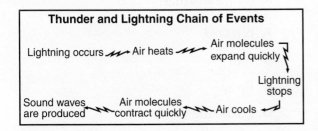

1 Which of these statements is correct?

A Thunder is electricity.

B Thunder comes before lightning.

C Lightning causes thunder.

D Air molecules change into lightning.

2 With which of these would you expect to find very high winds?

F rain

G hurricane

H snow

J flood

3 Humidity is the amount of moisture in the air. What would cause the humidity to decrease?

A thunderstorms

B snow

C rain

D drought

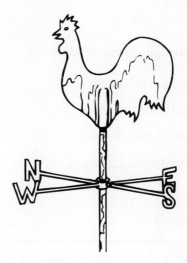

4 The picture above shows a device that helps determine the

F amount of rain

G wind speed

H direction of wind

J weather

GO ON ➡

5 Which sentence below might explain how lightning occurs?

A Oppositely charged air molecules attract and make light from electricity.

B High winds make air move so fast that it turns into light.

C Light from the sun reflects from the rain in quick bursts down to Earth's surface.

D Lightning comes from any type of storm.

6 Meteorologists use satellites to

F predict the weather

G diminish tornadoes

H change the weather

J determine vacation plans

7 Which of the following is <u>not</u> an example of severe weather?

A blizzard

B rain

C flood

D hurricane

8 A meteorologist has located a storm on radar. She would most likely use technology to determine

F where the storm is headed

G where the storm started

H when the storm started

J what areas have no storms

Directions: Read Number 9 below. Then, on the lines that follow, write your answer in complete sentences.

9 Design an experiment to collect data about how rain affects air temperature.

_____

_____

_____

_____

STOP

DIRECTIONS

Choose the best answer choice for each of the following questions.

1. Walruses live in polar climates. If the temperature of the climate changed and became warmer, which adaptation would NOT be appropriate for the new climate?

    a. tusks

    b. fins

    c. extra fat

    d. smooth skin

2. During El Niño, wind and precipitation patterns are affected around the world. Which of the following changes can occur as a result?

    f. floods in Australia and Africa

    g. storms in California

    h. droughts in the southern United States

    j. decrease in ocean temperatures

3. The most likely cause of an increase in Earth's temperature is _____.

    a. an increase in the amount of greenhouse gases

    b. an increase in the amount of energy from the sun

    c. a decrease in the atmospheric gases

    d. a hole in the ozone layer

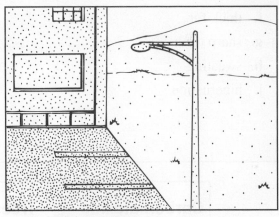

Heat Absorbed

4. Which area in the picture would contribute most to a temperature increase in the city?

    f. grassy area

    g. building

    h. light posts

    j. parking lot

GO ON ➡

5. Information about global warming would most likely be found under which heading in a table of contents?

    a. Solar Energy

    b. Seasonal Temperature Changes

    c. Greenhouse Effect

    d. Wind Patterns

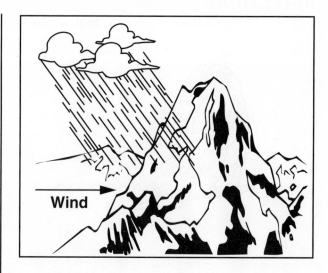

6. In general, the behavorial adaptation that provides animals the most benefit in the winter is _____.

    f. thick fur

    g. sharp teeth

    h. sweating

    j. hibernation

7. Which of these would form on the side of the mountain not facing the wind?

    a. lake

    b. glacier

    c. forest

    d. desert

Carbon dioxide in the air	→	Trees take in carbon dioxide	→	Amount of carbon dioxide decreases

8. Which of the following human activities would most affect the cycle shown above?

    f. burning fossil fuels

    g. deforestation

    h. pollution

    j. farming

STOP

DIRECTIONS

Read each question. Then, on your answer sheet, mark the answer choice that you think is best.

1 Over time, animals adapt to their environments. Which animal has adapted to life in the hot tropical zone?

  A snake

  B moose

  C penguin

  D snowy owl

2 Jerry's teacher gave him a rain gauge. He was able to use it to find out

  F how many clouds were in the area

  G how much rain had fallen

  H the average temperature

  J the level of rain pollution

3 We can help reduce the amount of energy used by changing simple things in our lives. Which of these would help save energy?

  A watch less television

  B keep lights on at night

  C drive instead of walk

  D drink more water

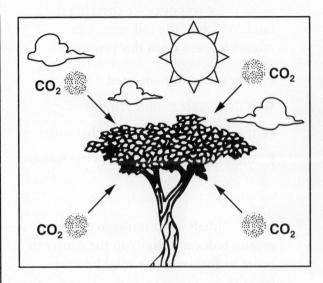

4 Which statement about trees is true?

  F They release carbon dioxide into the atmosphere.

  G They use sunlight to clean the air.

  H They do not play a role in the carbon dioxide cycle.

  J They help reduce the amount of carbon dioxide in the air.

5 Areas closer to the equator receive the most direct sunlight. Therefore, areas far from the equator probably

  A receive a lot of rain

  B often have storms and tornadoes

  C are not as warm

  D are more sunny

GO ON ➡

Standardized Test Practice   Chapter 17 *Climate*

6 Scientists have found rock layers that show there was once ice covering the land. Which of the following can scientists learn from this process?

   F how many animals lived

   G if there were people around

   H the climate of the area at that time

   J what the climate will be in the future

7 Some animals must undergo a time of greatly reduced activity in the winter in order to survive. They might do this because

   A it makes them grow bigger

   B they have nothing to do

   C they are tired

   D there is not enough food

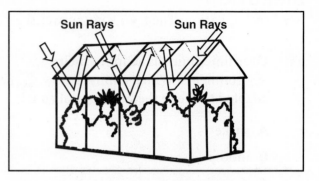

8 The picture shows how a greenhouse traps energy from the Sun. If Earth's atmosphere acted similarly, what would happen to our climate?

   F many more plants would grow

   G an ice age would occur

   H it might get warmer

   J nothing would change

Directions: Read Number 9 below. Then, on the lines that follow, write your answer in complete sentences.

9 Trees are important because they remove carbon dioxide from the air and release oxygen. They are also home to many types of living things. Humans have cut down many forests. What positive and negative effects could this have?

_____

_____

_____

_____

_____

_____

_____

STOP

DIRECTIONS

Choose the best answer choice for each of the following questions.

1. The most likely cause of the Gulf Stream in the Atlantic Ocean is the motion caused by _____.
   a. wind only
   b. gravitational effects of the Moon
   c. wind and Earth's rotation
   d. different densities of water in the Atlantic Ocean

2. Which of these contributes most to creating low tides?
   f. water density
   g. gravity
   h. weak winds
   j. water evaporation

3. A person is rowing a boat in the ocean one km off the nearest shoreline. There are many waves in the ocean that day. If all other factors are equal, the distance that each wave moves the rowboat _____.
   a. depends on the wavelength
   b. depends on the density of current speeds
   c. is equal to the strength of the tide
   d. would be only up and down but not forward

Ocean Water at 20°C	Ocean Water at 1°C
	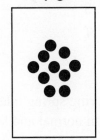

4. According to the diagram, which statement best describes what happens to ocean water when it is cooled?
   f. It moves faster than warmer water.
   g. It is more dense than warmer water.
   h. It will rise above warmer water.
   j. It is less dense than warmer water.

GO ON ➡

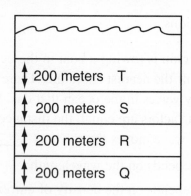

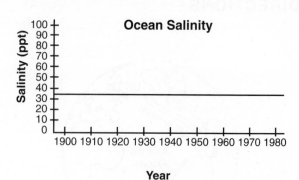

Year

5. The diagram shows a cross-section of the Atlantic Ocean. Which level most likely has the coldest water?

    a. Q

    b. R

    c. S

    d. T

6. During spring tides, high tides are higher than normal and low tides are lower than normal. What is the most likely cause of spring tides?

    f. the Sun, Earth, and Moon forming a right angle

    g. an increase in wind speed

    h. the Sun, Earth, and Moon line up

    j. an increase in the ocean's salinity

7. The graph above shows the average ocean salinity over an 80-year period. A reasonable conclusion based on these data is that over time _____.

    a. the average ocean salinity has increased

    b. the average ocean salinity has remained constant

    c. the average ocean salinity has decreased

    d. the average ocean salinity has remained in a state of unbalance

8. What has been the greatest benefit of desalination?

    f. increased production of salt

    g. increased ocean water density

    h. greater amount of mineral resources

    j. greater amount of drinking water

STOP

Chapter 18 *Ocean Motion*   **Standardized Test Practice**

DIRECTIONS

Read each question. Then, on your answer sheet, mark the answer choice that you think is best.

1 **Which statement provides the best description of density currents?**

  A They move faster than surface currents.

  B They occur only in the Pacific Ocean.

  C They move very slowly.

  D They are primarily formed in Antarctica.

2 **Which of the following is true about the Gulf Stream?**

  F It moves in an eastward direction.

  G It is 1000 kilometers wide.

  H It moves in a westward direction

  J It is located in the Gulf of Mexico.

3 **In what area of the world would you expect the difference between high and low tides to be hardly noticeable?**

  A the Atlantic coast of the United States

  B near the equator

  C Antarctica

  D the South Pole

4 **Approximately what percentage of Earth's surface is covered by water?**

  F 33 percent

  G 50 percent

  H 70 percent

  J 90 percent

5 **Which statement provides the best description of why a wave breaks?**

  A The bottom of the wave moves faster than the top.

  B Wind speed pushes the top of the wave over.

  C The bottom of the wave moves slower than the top.

  D The top of the wave has a greater concentration of salt than the bottom.

GO ON

Directions: Read Numbers 6–7 below. Then, on the lines that follow, write your answers in complete sentences.

6 Scientists aren't exactly sure how Earth's oceans were formed. Discuss one of the main scientific hypotheses about how Earth's oceans were formed billions of years ago.

_____

_____

_____

_____

_____

_____

_____

7 Water in the ocean is constantly in motion. Discuss the similarities and differences between various types of ocean currents.

_____

_____

_____

_____

_____

_____

_____

STOP

DIRECTIONS
Choose the best answer choice for each of the following questions.

1. Sewage is a type of water pollution that causes algae to reproduce at a rapid rate. Huge numbers of bacteria then reproduce and decompose the algae. When the algae die, animals such as fish also die in large numbers. Which of these is the most likely cause of the fish dying as the bacteria decompose the algae?

   a. The algae block the fish's gills.

   b. The bacteria is poisonous to the fish.

   c. Sunlight is not able to penetrate the algae.

   d. The bacteria uses up most of the oxygen.

2. Under which heading in a table of contents would the most information about the deposits that fill in the valleys in the seafloor be found?

   f. Continental Slope

   g. Abyssal Plains

   h. Trenches

   j. Benthos

3. All of these are examples of zooplankton EXCEPT _____.

   a. eggs

   b. jellyfish

   c. crabs

   d. diatoms

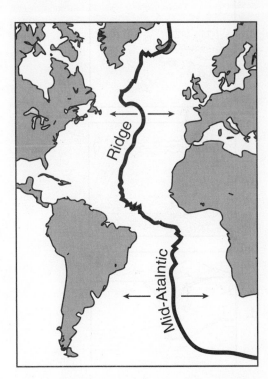

4. Along the Mid-Atlantic Ridge, new ocean floor is formed at a rate of approximately 2.5 cm per year. The most likely cause of the creation of this new ocean floor is the _____.

   f. deposition of sediment in the ocean

   g. movement of lava through cracks in Earth's crust

   h. erosion of the continental shelf

   j. movement of lava into the ocean from land volcanoes

GO ON ➡

5. All of these are examples of ocean margin habitats EXCEPT _____.

a.

b.

c.
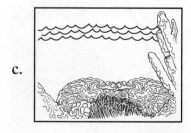

d.

6. Which of these is necessary for the process of photosynthesis in ocean plants?

   f. water, oxygen, and light energy

   g. carbon dioxide, magnesium, and light energy

   h. water, carbon dioxide, and light energy

   j. water, oxygen, and carbon dioxide

7. What is the purpose of building fixed platforms in the ocean?

   a. to mine for phosphorite and limestone

   b. to search for fresh drinking water

   c. to perform scientific experiments below the sea bed

   d. to pump oil from under the sea bed

STOP

DIRECTIONS

Read each question. Then, on your answer sheet, mark the answer choice that you think is best.

1 More fish develop into adults in estuaries than in oceans because

   A the water has more salt in it

   B there are fewer predators and more food

   C the water temperature is warmer

   D there are more predators and more food

2 Which statement provides the best description of a marine food chain?

   F All marine animals only consume plants.

   G It is less complex than land food chains.

   H Energy is transferred from organism to organism

   J Organisms that perform photosynthesis are called consumers.

3 What role do marine plants play in an ocean food chain?

   A consumer

   B producer

   C decomposer

   D composer

4 In which of these areas of an ocean would you expect to find the greatest amount of nutrients and marine organisms?

   F a beach

   G the ocean bottom

   H the continental shelf

   J mid-ocean

GO ON ➡

Standardized Test Practice   Chapter 19 *Oceanography*

5 Which of the following is <u>not</u> an example of pollution?

     A herbicides

     B benthos

     C sewage

     D silt

6 Which of the following is <u>not</u> an example of a nekton?

     F blue whale

     G jellyfish

     H tiger shark

     J swordfish

Directions: Read Numbers 7–8 below. Then, on the lines that follow, write your answers in complete sentences.

7 Just like landforms, the ocean basin is constantly changing. Discuss some of the ways that the ocean basin changes over time.

_____

_____

_____

_____

_____

8 Most of the water in our oceans is polluted in some way. Discuss the various ways in which human activities pollute our oceans. Include some of the ways people can help control pollution.

_____

_____

_____

_____

_____

_____

STOP

DIRECTIONS

Choose the best answer choice for each of the following questions.

Average Number of People per Square Kilometer of Land

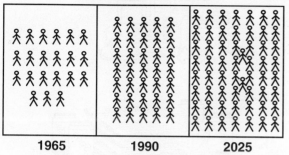

1965   **1990**   **2025**

1. According to the diagram, which statement best describes population growth in the United States?

   a. After an all-time high in the mid-1960s, the United States population has continued to drop.

   b. The population of the United States is expected to drop in the future, in spite of recent rises.

   c. The population of the United States has risen since the 1960s and is expected to continue to do so.

   d. In spite of a drop from the years 1965 to 1990, the United States population is expected to rise in the future.

2. Government regulation has forced automobile manufacturers to produce cars that get better gas mileage than those produced in the past. Which has been the greatest benefit of this improved gas mileage?

   f. developing recycling programs

   g. improving traffic safety

   h. raising new car prices

   j. conserving energy resources

3. Juan's class wanted to begin a school recycling program by collecting the glass bottles and aluminum cans used by students during lunchtime. Since drink containers must be sorted before recycling, which set of bins below would be most helpful?

GO ON ➡

4. In which of the following book chapters would you be most likely to find information about composting?

   f. Benefits of Recycling

   g. Human Population Growth

   h. Common Water Pollutants

   j. Yard Wastes and Decomposition

5. Which of the following methods of insect pest control would have the LEAST harmful effect on the environment?

   a. pulling out all the plants that the insect pests feed on

   b. spraying pesticides over all the plants

   c. setting traps that contain concentrated insecticide

   d. releasing insects that prey on the insect pests

PLASTIC GLASS ALUMINUM

6. Which of the following should be included in the box above?

   f. paper

   g. plants

   h. pesticides

   j. pollutants

7. Which of the following shows a group of items suitable for composting?

a.

b.

c.

d.

STOP

DIRECTIONS

Read each question. Then, on your answer sheet, mark the answer choice that you think is best.

1 Which of the following natural resources is renewable?

  A coal

  B natural gas

  C oil

  D water

The Tiger's Shrinking Range

Russia
Mongolia
China
India
Siberian Tiger (150-200)
South China Tiger (30-80)
Indo-Chinese Tiger (1,000-1,700)
Bengal Tiger (3,350-4,700)
Sumatran Tiger (650)

Key
Range in 1900   Range in 1994

2 The diagram above shows the shrinking ranges and estimated population of five different species of tiger. In the region of the world shown on the map, the danger of extinction would be greatest for the

  F Indo-Chinese tiger

  G Siberian tiger

  H South China tiger

  J Sumatran tiger

3 In the past, many buildings were insulated with asbestos because it was fireproof. Today, asbestos is being removed from buildings at great expense. Which of these is the most important reason for removing asbestos?

  A Asbestos has been identified as a cancer-causing agent.

  B Other materials are better insulators and less costly than asbestos.

  C Asbestos is now valuable as a component of microchip circuits.

  D Exposed asbestos is an eyesore.

4 Which of the following is <u>not</u> a fossil fuel?

  F oil

  G coal

  H natural gas

  J uranium

5 Pesticides sprayed on farmlands can get into rivers and streams as part of the runoff that follows a heavy rain. The concentration of these chemicals is usually measured in

  A percent

  B parts per million

  C milligrams

  D milliliters

GO ON ➡

6   The biggest problem with using plastic garbage bags is that they

     F   are expensive compared to paper bags

     G   often break when they are overfilled

     H   do not decompose when they are thrown away in a landfill

     J   produce toxic gases when they are burned by waste departments

Directions: Read Number 7 below. Then, on the lines that follow, write your answer in complete sentences.

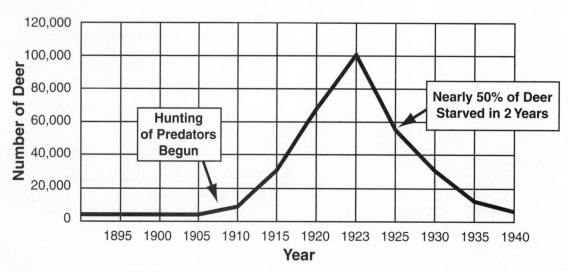

7   In 1906, President Theodore Roosevelt was advised that the deer population in a national forest was too low. To create more favorable conditions for the deer, he lifted a ban on the hunting of wolves, coyotes, and mountain lions, all of which prey on deer. The graph above shows how the deer population changed after hunting began. Between 1923 and 1925, nearly 50 percent of the deer population starved to death. Explain why this happened.

_____

_____

_____

_____

_____

_____

_____

DIRECTIONS

Choose the best answer choice for each of the following questions.

Air Quality Index

AQI Index Values	Health Categories	Cautionary Statements for 8-Hour Ozone
0 to 50	Good	None
51 to 100	Moderate	Sensitive people should consider limiting prolonged outdoor exertion.
101 to 150	Unhealthy for Sensitive Groups	Active children and adults and people with respiratory disease, such as asthma, should limit prolonged outdoor exertion.
151 to 200	Unhealthy	Active children and adults and people with respiratory disease, such as asthma, should limit prolonged outdoor exertion. Everyone else, especially children, should limit prolonged outdoor exertion.
201 to 300	Very Unhealthy	Active children and adults and people with respiratory disease, such as asthma, should limit prolonged outdoor exertion. Everyone else, especially children, should limit outdoor exertion.

1. According to the Air Quality Index, air with an AQI Value of 250 would have a rating of _____.

   a. moderate

   b. unhealthy

   c. very unhealthy

   d. hazardous

2. Students at a local high school voted to use reusable forks, knives, and spoons in their school cafeteria in place of throwaway plastic forks, knives, and spoons. What will most likely be the greatest benefit of this change?

   f. The school will use more hot water.

   g. Less trash will be sent to the landfill.

   h. The cafeteria will need to hire more workers.

   j. Less time will be needed to clean up after lunch.

GO ON ➡

Pollutants Emitted by Automobiles

Pollutant	Millions of Tons Per Year
Hydrocarbons	18
Carbon monoxide	65
Nitrogen oxides	8
Sulfur oxides	1
Other particles	2

3. The chart shows the amount of five pollutants emitted by automobiles every year. Which of these graphs best represents these data?

a.
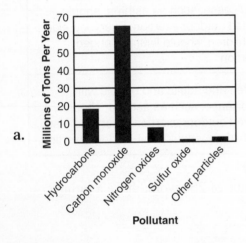

c.
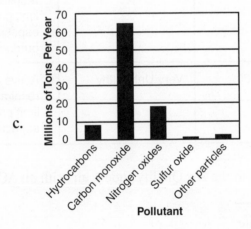

b.
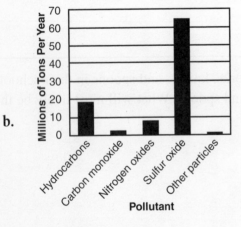

d.
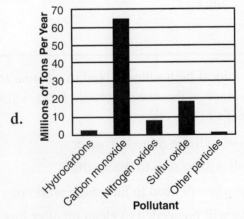

DIRECTIONS
Read each question. Then, on your answer sheet, mark the answer choice that you think is best.

1 Nuclear wastes are often buried under the ground in metal drums. The biggest problem with this practice is that the nuclear wastes may

   A leak into the ground and enter groundwater that supplies drinking water

   B increase the rate of chemical weathering in the soil surrounding the drums

   C change local weather conditions

   D react with surrounding chemicals and explode

2 Oil is an example of an energy source that formed from the remains of dead plants and animals hundreds of millions of years ago. These energy sources are called

   F nuclear fuels

   G renewable resources

   H fossil fuels

   J alternative energy sources

3 The human nasal cavity is lined with mucus and small hairs. This helps humans by

   A filtering out harmful particles from inhaled air

   B absorbing oxygen from the air into the blood

   C removing carbon dioxide from the blood

   D cooling off air inhaled in hot weather

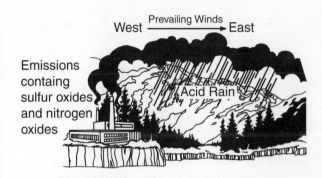

4 Harmful gases produced by the burning of fossil fuels combine with moisture in the air to form acid rain. Which of these tactics would most reduce the formation of acid rain?

   F improve weather forecasting

   G introduce new fish into lakes and streams

   H decrease the amount of moisture in the air

   J filter out harmful gases before they enter the air

5 Which of the following is <u>not</u> an example of biological control of environmental problems?

   A the use of bacteria to infect and destroy the gypsy moth in its caterpillar stage

   B the spraying of pesticides over crops in order to destroy insect pests

   C the introduction of ladybugs to prey on aphids that are eating crops

   D the use of microorganisms that produce enzymes capable of digesting oil spills

GO ON ➡

6 Which of these pollutants is responsible for the depletion of the ozone layer in Earth's atmosphere?

F sulfur dioxide from the burning of fossil fuels

G carbon monoxide from automobile exhaust

H chlorofluorocarbons (CFCs) from air conditioners and refrigerators

J photochemical smog from the reaction of nitrogen oxides with sunlight

7 Which statement provides the best description of point-source pollution?

A Pollution that enters a body of water over a large area.

B Pollution from a source that cannot be identified.

C Pollution that enters water from acid rain.

D Pollution that enters water from a specific location.

Directions: Read Numbers 8–9 below. Then, on the lines that follow, write your answers in complete sentences.

8 Explain the steps you should take to dispose of wastes safely.

_____

_____

_____

_____

9 Explain how acid rain forms. List the effects of acid rain on buildings, wildlife, and plant life.

_____

_____

_____

_____

STOP

DIRECTIONS

Choose the best answer choice for each of the following questions.

Some Space Probe Missions

Date	Mission	Purpose
1977	*Voyager 1*	To fly past Jupiter and Saturn
1977	*Voyager 2*	To fly past Jupiter, Saturn, Uranus, and Neptune
1989	*Galileo*	To transmit information about Jupiter and its moons back to Earth
1992	*Mars Observer*	To collect information about Mars (mission failed)

1. According to the chart, the space probe most likely to have collected pictures about Uranus would be _____.

   a. *Voyager 1*

   b. *Voyager 2*

   c. *Galileo*

   d. *Mars Observer*

Types of Spacecraft

Type	Example	Description
Space Station	*Skylab 1*	A spacecraft with supplies and areas for humans staying a long time in space.
Satellite	*Sputnik 1*	An object that revolves around another object.
Probe	*Pathfinder*	An instrument that sends information from space back to Earth.
Space Shuttle	*Columbia*	A spacecraft that can carry people and objects into and back from space.

2. According to the chart, a spacecraft that is designed to take pictures of planets for scientists back on Earth is _____.

   f. a space station

   g. a satellite

   h. a probe

   j. a space shuttle

GO ON ➡

Chapter Test   Chapter 22 *Exploring Space*

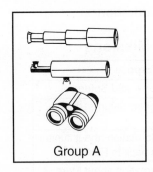

Group A

Group B

3. The instruments in Group A are different from the instruments in Group B because only the instruments in Group A are _____.

    a. objects that produce visible light

    b. objects that can be found in school classrooms

    c. tools for observing visible light coming from a distance

    d. tools for measuring the temperature of very hot objects

4. A reflecting telescope uses a mirror. Which of the following is a reflecting telescope?

    f.

    g.

    h.

    j.

5. Which of the following has been the greatest benefit of using the space shuttle?

    a. transporting astronauts and materials to and from space

    b. exploring the surfaces of Mars and Jupiter

    c. disposing of the space shuttle after one mission

    d. using solar energy to power spaceships

6. Under which heading in a table of contents would the most information about the *Apollo 11* space mission be found?

    f. The Space Shuttle

    g. Telescopes: Looking up into Space

    h. The Race to the Moon

    j. Satellites

DIRECTIONS

Read each question. Then, on your answer sheet, mark the answer choice that you think is best.

1 The weights of astronauts are much less when they walk on the Moon than when they walk on Earth. This is because of

A the depth of the Moon's craters

B the light coming from the Sun

C the strength of the Moon's gravity

D the solar winds

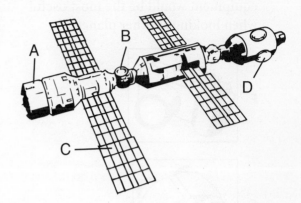

2 Some kinds of telescopes contain lenses. The lens of a telescope

F magnifies and focuses the light

G reflects the light back out to space

H turns the telescope off and on

J moves the telescope up and down

4 In the picture of the International Space Station, the most likely place to put solar panels to generate electricity would be

F A

G B

H C

J D

3 While walking on the Moon, the astronauts' space suits keep them alive by

A keeping them at the right pressure and temperature

B giving them food to eat

C providing pockets for carrying Moon rocks

D preventing them from tripping

5 Space probes have been used by scientists for many years. Space probes can be used to

A carry astronauts to the space station

B fly to distant planets to take pictures

C carry astronauts working on experiments

D house teams working in space for months

GO ON ▶

6 Which of the following pieces of equipment would be the most useful when looking at other planets?

F

G

H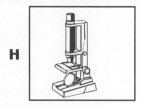

J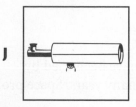

7 Which of the following is considered a type of electromagnetic radiation?

A light

B water

C wind

D ozone

Directions: Read Number 8 below. Then, on the lines that follow, write your answer in complete sentences.

8 In the past, the United States and the former Soviet Union competed and cooperated to reach the goals of their space programs. Explain how the race to reach the Moon and the creation of the new International Space Station support this statement.

_____

_____

_____

_____

_____

STOP

DIRECTIONS

Choose the best answer choice for each of the following questions.

1. The gradual change in the length of your shadow over the course of the day is caused by _____.

   a. the revolution of Earth around the Sun

   b. the rotation of Earth on its axis

   c. the revolution of the Moon around Earth

   d. the rotation of the Moon on its axis

2. The effect of the Sun is strongest when the Sun is directly overhead. At which of the times listed below would a person who sunburns easily be best advised to stay indoors?

   f. 8 A.M.

   g. 12 noon

   h. 4 P.M.

   j. 8 P.M.

3. The gravitational pull of the Moon has a greater effect than the pull of the Sun on the tidal changes in Earth's oceans. The most likely reason for this is _____.

   a. the Sun is closer to Earth

   b. the Moon is closer to Earth

   c. the Sun is larger than the Moon

   d. Earth is larger than the Moon

4. Which of the following occurs when Earth is positioned directly between the Sun and the Moon, making the Moon invisible to observers on Earth?

   f. a lunar eclipse

   g. a solar eclipse

   h. a full Moon

   j. a waxing Moon

5. The fact that Earth's axis is tilted 23.5° is responsible for _____.

   a. the change between day and night

   b. the changing of the seasons

   c. solar eclipses

   d. lunar eclipses

6. Which of these sources would be the most helpful to determine which telescope gives the best view of the stars?

   f. the prices of the telescopes

   g. the data from an objective test

   h. advertisements for the telescopes

   j. the colors of the telescopes

GO ON ▬▶

7. In a study of the Sun's location during solstices, which question would be the most important to answer?

   a. What is the Sun's distance north or south of the equator?

   b. How many scientists have studied solstices?

   c. Is the termperature at the equator affected by the Sun's location?

   d. How many hours of sunlight are there on the summer solstice?

8. An ellipse is an elongated, closed curve. According to this information, which of the following orbits is an ellipse?

   f.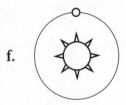

   g.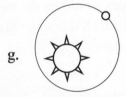

   h.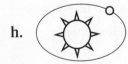

   j.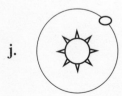

9. Which of the following occurs when the Sun is directly above Earth's equator?

   a. equinox

   b. solstice

   c. new moon

   d. eclipse

10. Which of the following best describes an impact basin?

   f. the white glow around the edges of the Moon

   g. a round, three-dimensional object

   h. the hollow left behind by an object striking the Moon

   j. an elongated, closed curve

11. Early data from the *Lunar Prospector* indicated the presence of hydrogen in crater rocks at the Moon's poles. According to this data, what is the most likely theory that could be made?

   a. The Moon's core is 600 kilometers in diameter.

   b. Ice may exist in the floors of craters at the Moon's poles.

   c. Ice may exist in the floors of craters only at the Moon's north pole.

   d. Water may exist 600 kilometers under the Moon's surface.

STOP

DIRECTIONS

Read each question. Then, on your answer sheet, mark the answer choice that you think is best.

1 The largest crater on the Moon is 12 kilometers deep and 2,500 kilometers in diameter. If craters are caused by large objects striking the lunar surface, the crater was probably caused by a

A pebble

B planet

C galaxy

D meteorite

2 Which of the following diagrams depicts a lunar eclipse?

F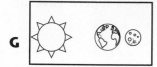

G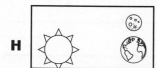

H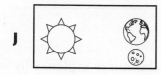

J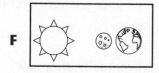

3 Which of the diagrams below depicts an equinox?

A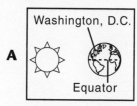

B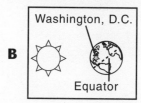

C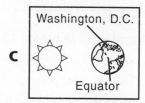

D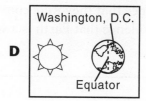

4 The diameter of Earth would best be measured using what units?

F centimeters

G kilometers

H kilograms

J inches

GO ON ➡

5 Renah is painting her house. What color should she paint it so that it will reflect the most light from the Sun?

  A white

  B orange

  C green

  D black

6 The Moon is visible to us because the Moon

  F reflects light from the Sun

  G reflects light from Earth

  H produces light through fusion

  J produces light through combustion

Directions: Read Numbers 7–8 below. Then, on the lines that follow, write your answers in complete sentences.

7 For thousands of years, people were convinced that Earth was flat. Eventually, they saw enough evidence that they were convinced that Earth was shaped like a sphere. Give an example of evidence that Earth is a sphere.

_____

_____

_____

_____

8 Use what you know about the positions of Earth, the Moon, and the Sun to explain why we see different phases of the Moon.

_____

_____

_____

_____

STOP

DIRECTIONS

Choose the best answer choice for each of the following questions.

Characteristics of Some Planets

Planet	Distance from the Sun (millions of kilometers)	Diameter (km)
Mercury	58	4,880
Venus	108	12,104
Earth	149	12,756
Mars	228	6,787

1. According to this information, which planet is more than 200 million kilometers from the Sun?

   a. Mercury

   b. Venus

   c. Earth

   d. Mars

2. What has been the greatest benefit of sending probes out into the solar system?

   f. providing detailed information about the other planets

   g. improving the quality of communication systems on Earth

   h. explaining the factors that cause changes in the weather

   j. finding new materials for use in industry

3. Lisa wanted to observe the planet Jupiter with a telescope. Under which of the following conditions would she best be able to do this?

   a. a day with a clear sky

   b. a night with a clear sky

   c. a rainy day

   d. a rainy night

4. George's parents warned him not to stare directly at the Sun during a solar eclipse. Why did they give him that warning?

   f. The Sun is always hidden behind clouds during an eclipse.

   g. Staring at the Sun during an eclipse damages the eyes.

   h. Eclipses happen often, and George will be able to see another.

   j. The Moon blocks the view of the Sun during an eclipse.

GO ON ➡

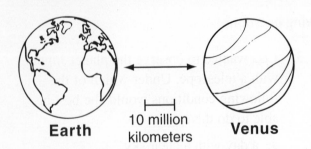

Earth   10 million kilometers   **Venus**

5. Approximately how far apart are Venus and Earth in the picture above?

    a. 30 million kilometers

    b. 40 million kilometers

    c. 50 million kilometers

    d. 60 million kilometers

VENUS MARS NEPTUNE

6. Which of the following belongs in the group above?

    f. The Milky Way

    g. Titan

    h. Sirius

    j. Mercury

Earth's Tilt	Toward Sun		Away from Sun		Toward Sun
Season	Summer	Fall	Winter	Spring	Summer

7. According to the chart, when the northern hemisphere of Earth is tilted away from the Sun, the season will be _____.

    a. spring

    b. summer

    c. fall

    d. winter

8. A science class has studied the characteristics of different asteroids. Which of the following is the best explanation for an asteroid with many craters?

    f. Craters are revealed when an asteroid's crust burns up in the atmosphere.

    g. Craters were made when the asteroid was collected by scientists.

    h. The asteroid has had many collisions over a long period of time.

    j. The asteroid is composed of very fragile materials.

STOP

DIRECTIONS
Read each question. Then, on your answer sheet, mark the answer choice that you think is best.

1 A scientist is attempting to classify a large object in space. The scientist has determined that the object is in orbit around the planet Jupiter. The object is most likely a

A planet

B star

C moon

D meteor

2 Which of the following would be measured using kilometers?

F the diameter of Mars

G the weight of Mars

H the density of Mars

J the age of Mars

3 People who see meteors burning up in Earth's atmosphere often confuse them with stars. The objects that people refer to as shooting stars are actually meteors. People probably confuse meteors with stars because meteors

A appear as tiny, bright lights in the sky

B are as large as stars

C are pieces that break off from comets

D travel at very high speeds

4 Which of the diagrams below shows the three planets in the correct order of their distance from the Sun?

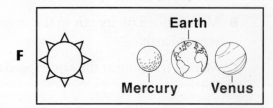

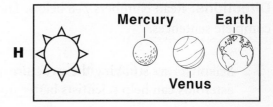

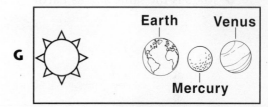

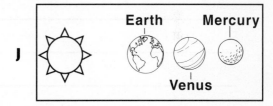

GO ON ➡

Standardized Test Practice   Chapter 24 *The Solar System*

5 The planet Mars has seasons similar to those on Earth. The most likely reason for this is

   A Mars is the same distance from the Sun as the Earth

   B Mars is tilted on its axis in the same way as Earth

   C Mars is traveling at the same speed as Earth

   D Mars is the same size as Earth

6 Using sunblock at the beach protects your skin by

   F keeping your body dry

   G providing important nutrients

   H stopping solar radiation from affecting your skin

   J making the surface of your skin smoother and moister

Directions: Read Numbers 7–8 below. Then, on the lines that follow, write your answers in complete sentences.

7 Scientists are studying the structure and composition of asteroids. Explain how studying asteroids can help scientists better understand how Earth was formed.

_____

_____

_____

8 A year is defined as the time it takes for a planet to make one revolution around the Sun. Use what you know about the positions of the planets to explain why a year on Mars is nearly twice as long as a year on Earth.

_____

_____

_____

_____

STOP

DIRECTIONS
Choose the best answer choice for each of the following questions.

Main Sequence Stars

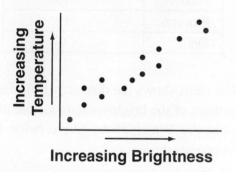

Increasing Brightness

1. The graph shows the relationship between temperature and brightness for Main Sequence stars. What is a reasonable hypothesis that can be drawn from these data?

   a. Hotter stars will have more surrounding planets than cooler stars.

   b. Hotter stars last longer than cooler stars.

   c. Cooler stars will be less bright than hotter stars.

   d. Cooler stars are denser than hotter stars.

2. The Sun and the star Alpha Centauri shine with about the same brightness, yet the Sun appears to us to be several hundred times brighter than Alpha Centauri. Which of these is the most likely explanation for this?

   f. Alpha Centauri is a larger star than the Sun.

   g. The Sun generates energy through the process of fusion.

   h. The Sun is much closer to Earth than Alpha Centauri.

   j. Light from Alpha Centauri is blocked by the Moon.

Layers of the Sun's Atmosphere

Height	Name
Surface to 100 km	Photosphere
100 km to 2,000 km	Chromosphere
2,000 km to 10,000 km	Transition Zone
Above 10,000 km	Corona

3. According to the table, a height of 1,800 kilometers above the surface of the Sun will be part of which section of the Sun's atmosphere?

   a. photosphere

   b. chromosphere

   c. transition zone

   d. corona

GO ON ➡

WHITE DWARF   SUPERGIANT   NEUTRON STAR

4. Which of the following belongs with the group above?

   f. asteroid

   g. planet

   h. supernova

   j. galaxy

5. Scientists have identified different types of galaxies. Which question would be the LEAST important to ask when identifying a galaxy's type?

   a. Does the galaxy have spiral arms?

   b. How large is the galaxy?

   c. What is the shape of the galaxy?

   d. Does the galaxy orbit the Milky Way?

The Brightest Stars

Star	Distance (light-years)
Altair	16
Procyon	11
Sirius	9

6. The chart shows the distances from Earth to three of the brightest stars visible in the night sky. Which of the graphs below best represents these data?

f.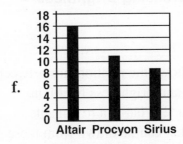

g.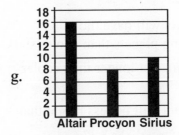

h.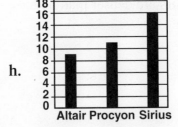

j.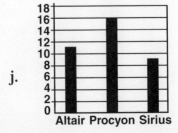

STOP

DIRECTIONS

Read each question. Then, on your answer sheet, mark the answer choice that you think is best.

1 In the core of a star, the temperature can reach heights unknown on Earth. The process by which stars generate energy is called

   A photosynthesis

   B fusion

   C condensation

   D radiation

2 An astronomer measured the distance between two stars. The distance the astronomer recorded was probably measured in

   F light-years

   G centimeters

   H tons

   J inches

3 Dan viewed two light bulbs of equal power. Bulb A appeared dimmer than Bulb B. A possible explanation for this is that

   A Bulb B is farther away from Dan than Bulb A

   B Bulb A is farther away from Dan than Bulb B

   C Bulb A and Bulb B are next to each other

   D Bulb A and Bulb B are connected to the same battery

4 The Milky Way galaxy is visible from Earth most clearly when no other light is present. Which of the following is the best situation for viewing the Milky Way galaxy?

   F in a large city at night

   G in a large city during the day

   H in a rural area at night

   J in a rural area during the day

5 Which of the following objects is closest to Earth?

   A the Moon

   B the Sun

   C the planet Mars

   D the planet Jupiter

6 Which of the following inventions had the greatest effect on the study of astronomy?

   F microscopes

   G automobiles

   H antibiotics

   J telescopes

GO ON ➡

7 An object that allows absolutely no light to escape would appear to be what color?

   A black

   B yellow

   C blue

   D white

8 In which of these would you expect to find a large number of stars?

   F the solar system

   G the rings of Saturn

   H the asteroid belt

   J the Milky Way galaxy

Directions: Read Numbers 9–10 below. Then, on the lines that follow, write your answers in complete sentences.

9 Two stars are shining with equal power, but to an observer on Earth, one star seems to be shining brighter than the other. What is a possible explanation for this?

_____

_____

_____

_____

_____

10 According to the Doppler effect, when an object is moving away from an observer, the light from that object will undergo a red shift. Explain how this effect could be used to show that the universe is expanding.

_____

_____

_____

_____

STOP